Words After Dark

A Lyrics, Lit & Liquor Anthology

Edited by Amanda Miller
& Amy Dupcak

Contents

Intro

A Note from Amanda

When my writing group member, Scott Hess, hosted a variety show for his book launch at Bluestockings Bookstore on Manhattan's Lower East Side in the spring of 2012, I was inspired: live music, a short film, solo theater and mixed genre readings. I LOVE variety shows. Experiencing a range of voices, art forms, and emotions in a single evening feels exceedingly satisfying to me, akin to a full body massage (in addition to being a writer, I'm an actor, comedian *and* massage therapist). At the time of Scott's launch I'd been hosting a comedy variety show for a couple of years at the Parkside Lounge—a dive bar with a back room just a few blocks from Bluestockings—but I'd never attended a variety show in which literature was featured let alone the centerpiece of the evening. I also found that breaking up the readings with other forms of art helped audiences listen more deeply.

For a while I'd been straddling the performance and literary worlds, but Scott helped me see a way to bridge the two. A chapter from my memoir *One Breath, Then Another* was due out in an anthology that August and I decided to host an event to celebrate its publication at Parkside Lounge with a reading of my chapter between various acts. I booked other readers, comedians, and a singer-songwriter, packing the room. It was a memorable night, moving from the hilarious to the heartbreaking with lush tunes interspersed throughout. Afterward, The Lounge invited me to host an ongoing show in this format and, with that, Lyrics, Lit & Liquor was born. My writing group, the Ponies, helped me come up with the name (who doesn't love alliteration?). While other performances would be sprinkled in, readings and music would form the show's backbone.

The most important thing was to have a fun, welcoming, unpretentious, DIY feel open to a wide array of writers, musicians, and performers, with no fancy credits or a book deal required. I would book performers through my pool of artist friends and acquaintances, send invitations to people I'd seen perform at other events, and accept word-of-mouth recommendations, sometimes placing open calls in my writer and performer social media groups. I would serve as the laid back, goofy host to make the audience feel cozy and at home.

A discussion about the series with dear friend, fellow Pony, and *Jeopardy!* fan Amy Dupcak led to the idea to include original themed trivia at every show, a question between each performance. We thought it would be a fun way to keep the audience engaged throughout the night and we would make it optional for performers to share work on that night's trivia theme. I would throw a piece of candy to each person who correctly answered a question. The premiere Lyrics, Lit & Liquor event took place on October 9, 2012 and our trivia theme was John Lennon, since it was his birthday. Folks packed the venue and all went as I'd hoped: a feeling of community, sharing art and lifting up one another.

With each proceeding show, Amy and I have come up with the theme together. Sometimes we connect it to a coinciding calendar event, but usually we come to it through brainstorming. Since aside from the trivia, most of the night's material doesn't fit the theme, I thread it through our event in other ways: a pre-show playlist, a theme-inspired sound collectively determined by the room to call out when someone knows an answer, and, in recent years, I've opened the show as a comedy character performing a themed song, monologue, dance, etc.

While we have changed venues four times in our nearly eight-year lifespan—from Parkside Lounge to Three of Cups to HiFi Bar to 2A, our current home—we've remained in the East Village. And while the overall vibe of that neighborhood has dramatically changed over the past decade, it's still hallowed ground for DIY alternative art and culture. We've always aimed to contribute to the spirit of a neighborhood that keeps that torch lit.

This anthology, *Words After Dark,* is a natural outgrowth of our series and the brainchild of myself and Amy Dupcak. We wanted to feature some of the talented readers and musicians who have graced our stage over the years, and to share their work with an even wider audience. Editing this anthology has been a labor of love nourished by a deep commitment to maintaining a space for open artistic expression and community. We originally intended to publish this anthology in May 2020 in tandem with a celebratory bash at Bar 2A. Alas, the Covid-19 pandemic shuttered venues, eliminated in-person gatherings and relegated us to the walls of our apartments for the indefinite future. And so we postponed our publication date, waiting until we could hold a proper release party in our proper venue. But as the pandemic has persisted with no clear indication as to when "normal life" will resume, we decided to publish now.

I owe a tremendous debt of gratitude to the arts, which have been getting me through life in a serious way since I was eleven. I have enormous respect for every artist who tenaciously continues to create, defying every conceivable obstacle, because their work sustains them and makes life worth living. And so it feels appropriate to be releasing *Words After Dark* during a global pandemic. Because artists are persistent little buggers, and our conditions have never really been optimal.

In closing, I am thrilled to present our humble collection of work. I am in love with all our contributors. Shout out to every writer, performer and musician who keeps at it. Never stop creating.

A Note from Amy

I feel so fortunate to work with the multitalented Amanda on this here anthology and on the Lyrics, Lit & Liquor series, which has afforded me the space to share my words (after dark), engage within a creative community, and contribute my lifelong passion for trivia.

As a kid, I practically memorized the *Guinness Book of World Records* (especially the Human Body section) and loved playing Trivial Pursuit with my dad. When I was five or six, he would always ask the questions—"What color is Grover's nose?"—and it never took long to fill my little plastic pie with wedges. But one day, I picked up a game card myself—"How tall is a regulation basketball hoop?"—and realized that he'd only been *pretending* to read off the cards, making up his own questions instead.

There's certainly an art to knowing your audience: too easy and the room erupts with whatever odd sound we invented for the night; too hard and the room falls utterly silent, until Amanda rereads the question more slowly and offers the hint I've supplied. I end up preparing eight to twelve questions on any one theme and try to provide a range in difficulty, from the relatively easy to the downright head-scratching, though it's not always possible to predict what the audience will know about a particular subject. I'm always pleasantly surprised when someone gets a tricky or obscure answer right away, and just as surprised when no one guesses correctly, even after a hint, which has only happened two or three times in our entire eight-year history.

What I love most about writing trivia is piquing the crowd's collective curiosity, encouraging them to rack their memories or rely on free-association as they surf the same wavelength. I love the pause before an answer materializes and the excited burst of energy with which hands shoot up. I love when everyone applauds the person who gets it right, and love watching Amanda hurl that coveted Twix from her perch on the stage. I love to make an entire room of friends and strangers work together by building off each other's incorrect assumptions, and love making them guess ridiculous things until someone stumbles onto the correct yet equally ridiculous (or scandalous!) answer. I love dropping useless knowledge on unsuspecting listeners, and love tumbling down internet rabbit holes in search of some little-known scientific, historical, or cultural fact that won't save my life but may come in handy when I least expect it.

Without further ado, here is the list of trivia themes, in no particular order, from every event we've held thus far: love, fashion, magic, science, fairy tales, dreams, New York, food, sex, games, psychology, the human body, escape from reality, awesome women, literary villains, one hit wonders, weather, geography, childhood, medicine, celebrations, John Lennon, name that song, name that movie, LGBTQ+, mythological creatures, outer space, firsts, cities, 1920s, summer, Asia, revolutions, the supernatural, visual art, grammar and words, animal kingdom, teen angst, banned books, Burning Man, ancient history, inventions and innovations, under the sea, and winning! You'll find a selection of past trivia questions at the start of every section; hope you enjoy answering them as much as I enjoyed writing them. Good luck!

Pale Ale

Trivia

1. Ossified, zozzled, splificated!—all 1920's slang for *this* word.

One Hit Wonders

2. Though the title of *this* one-hit-wonder appears nowhere in the lyrics, you'll hear about four alcoholic drinks and a whole lot of getting back up again.

Revolutions

3. At the height of the anti-war and hippie movements in the United States, *this* group of radical artists, intellectuals, and Marxists led a mass uprising to occupy universities and factories in Paris.

Summer

4. The hottest day of summer in Bed-Stuy, Brooklyn is the setting of *this* culturally relevant film from 1989.

Medicine

5. The Mad Hatter wasn't the only person poisoned by *this* chemical, once used in medicine as well as in the manufacture of Victorian felt hats; though today, you're more likely to be exposed to it by eating fish.

All trivia answers appear in the back of this book. No peeking!

Amanda Miller
fiction

The Open Mic

Dan's making jokes about his dick. "I'm going to cum all over your face!" he yells, straddling the mic stand. I'm not sure if this is a punch line to a set up I missed or just something he yells when he feels nervous. I've only been half listening, sinking deeper into my seat, trying to disappear further and further into the dark so he can't see my disgust. God, why did I fuck him after last week's mic? Because of the booze. Because he praised my set. Because it seemed like he understood me in a way so few of these cliché comics ever do. If he had gone up on stage last Monday, there's no way I would have gone home with him.

It's 7pm. The ten other people in Hank's Bar's tiny basement are drunk comedians, nine dudes and one other woman, all slouched either on the lumpy stained couch against the back wall or in the once white plastic lawn chairs scattered across the sticky floor. I recognize most of them from last week, and the week before that, and the week before that. Everyone is sitting as far back as possible, two rows of empty chairs lined up in front.

The door at the top of the stairs swings open so that the bar music gusts into the room before it's re-muffled. Three younger looking guys and one girl descend, whispering and giggling to each other, their requisite one-drink minimums in hand (mandatory for performers as well). They don't look sloppy or desperate enough to be comics; they must know someone going up tonight. Or they are drunk college students, checking out the New York dives. Those were the days.

This mic is like a group therapy session, but the worst kind: the kind where everyone is a total egomaniac and no one is listening to anyone else. It's group therapy where everyone is actually obsessed with their dysfunction and wants to revel in it instead of trying to get well. When did comedy become about the public contemplation of suicide?

I make it a rule to never talk about sex, heartbreak, or how much I hate myself, though of course I think about all three constantly. These thoughts are the root cause of why I take uptown trains from Canal Street when I mean to go to Brooklyn, or walk into walls, or drop my wallet on the tracks. Sex, heartbreak, and self-loathing are so obvious; I want to be more original than that to at least have a hair's worth of a shot at being remembered.

Derek went up before Dan. Now he's picking up his beer and heading upstairs. I'm tempted to follow him and forget about my set. My jokes suddenly all strike me as dumb, incomplete, pretentious. Maybe a better use of my time would be to go home and work on them, or drink myself to sleep. Most of the dudes in here are just fiddling with their phones anyway. At least Dan can't see because the spotlight is so blinding. We can only be honest with people we can't see. That's show biz.

The host, Max, flashes Dan the light, indicating he has one minute to wrap it up. One more minute until I get to martyr myself. If I bomb, I'll have an excuse to get wasted and fuck another sad comic. Jesus, if I want drunk sex that bad, I should probably just go on Tinder. I don't need to put myself through this. So why do I? It's probably because I'm a masochist. It must have something to do with my childhood days back on the farm in Kentucky, some traumatic incident involving my dad and a cow udder.

Dan finishes his last joke and I give a courtesy laugh, applauding even though I have no idea what the hell he's been talking about. Max gets up and shakes Dan's hand, the two of them looking pretty pleased with themselves. They may as well be swapping semen.

"Thanks, Dan," says Max, close enough to the mic to make it squeak. Everyone jumps in their seats; at least they'll be awake for my set. The three youngsters cackle, marking the greatest laughter spell of the night. Max glances at the set list scotch-taped to the sidewall.

"Next up, we have Miss Lauren Hauser. Give it up!" yells Max.

There's a flurry of light applause, like no one wants to clap too hard for fear of hurting their hands. I could be doing so many other things right now, like applying to law school or the seminary or petitioning a homeless man to finger me. Instead I rise calmly and wade through the musty air to the mic, taking my place under the light. The light seems brighter than I remember. Maybe the rapture is coming.

"Hi everyone," I hear myself say. That first sound of my voice projecting through the speakers gives me the familiar shot of self-importance that I know will leave as soon as I tell a joke that falls flat. And then the self-hatred will creep in, but I won't talk about it. I'll dutifully recite what I've prepared, knowing I can punish myself later. Stand up comedy might be the most unforgiving art form. Oh well. Fuck it. Here goes.

"Hi, I'm Lauren. So I don't know about you guys, but I am exhausted. Like in a way that goes so far beyond sleepy. In a way that makes me wonder if someone is putting horse tranquilizers in my food or roofying me on the daily. Last night I had a glass of wine at this bar and I woke up in the middle of the night passed out in my bathroom with my skirt over my head covered in Cheetos, with no memory...Wait, now that I'm talking about it, I do recall coming home, smoking weed, and taking an Ambien. But I swear those Cheetos are still a mystery."

Silence. They hate me. I can make a run for it. Nobody would come after me. Just flee up the stairs. But I keep going.

"People in England seem nice. That accent. It's so...polite. I've seriously been thinking about moving there, but I just can't get up the nerve."

Crickets...I hate myself.

"So...yeah...England. That makes me think of Amy Winehouse, another celebrity who supposedly had it all and died of alcohol poisoning. Make some noise if dying of alcohol poisoning sounds romantic to you."

Dan and Max hoot. Some other people laugh nervously.

"Yeah I used to think so too...until my mom died of it. Just kidding, she's still alive. She's in a nursing home on Long Island, doesn't know who the hell I am. Yells a lot for her mom who's been dead for two decades. That's where we're all heading, so you know, maybe it would be better to die of alcohol poisoning."

More silence. This one more cavernous and painful than the last. I decide to join in. I want to see how long it can go on before someone breaks.

The only sounds are faint noises through the door from the bar upstairs. Some people giggle nervously but no one says anything. I feel the heat from the spotlight. I exhale into the microphone and hear my breath. More nervous laughter. Max starts to stand. I raise my palm to signify I am not done. He sits slowly. I conduct a one-hundred-and-eighty-degree scan of the dark room before me. Since I'm in the light and they're in the dark, I'm responsible for what happens next.

I could do anything right now: scream, strip, pull out a hacksaw. I just continue to stare. My vision blurs. Someone coughs. Someone sets a glass on a table. Someone's feet hit the floor.

Then without warning, laughter bursts forth from my body, like a baby entering the world. As if on cue, the whole basement responds with explosive pain-in-the-belly guffaws. People are clutching their stomachs, the backs of their chairs, the shoulders of their neighbors. The laughing is interspersed with breath catching. I catch Dan and the college girl laughing while sucking face. The guy next to them wipes tears from his eyes and drops his iPhone. The screen cracks but his chortles don't stop. The entire beer-bellied ironic T-shirted pack is slapping something: knees, backs, chairs, tables. Bottles and glasses crash against the floor while everyone keeps making waves of that strange undulating sound: something like chimps mating while under attack. Gradually the laughing gives way to giggling, which gives way to snickers and finally, silence— back to where we began. But this silence feels different: comfortable, safe, satiated. We have all experienced the satisfaction of tension and release, no joke necessary.

"Once again, I'm Lauren Hauser," I say into the mic. "Thank you."

I step off the tiny termite infested stage, lit from within, counting down the days until next week's mic.

Jared Harél
poetry

You Want It Darker

The day after the election, Leonard Cohen dies
and my eye gets infected, and my daughter
flies around the living room refusing to put on underwear.
I can barely lift my head to see the smug sun
pouring through the blinds, streaming its white spotlight
on each darkened wall. I'm all in on grief and misery.
All in shock and *Fuck this Country*, but it's still a day, a day
I don't teach, but strap my son into his Cheerio-
encrusted stroller and wheel him to his 'baby-taps'
dance class at the Y. We arrive to find the teacher red-eyed
and wrecked, her t-shirt wrinkled, acoustic slung low.
Only one other parent has bothered to show,
her kid wailing beneath the moon-glow of her phone.
When it becomes clear no one else is coming,
the teacher begins to strum and sing of fall, of piggies
at market and monkeys in our beds. We squeeze
our fingers into spinning fists and imagine
we are busses peeling out of town. It all culminates
in the world's saddest rendition of "If you're happy
and you know it," in which we're summoned to rise up
off our multi-colored mats, to clap and stomp
and shout, *Hooray!* — Oh, God. Oh, Leonard,
who shed this life like a pinstripe suit, who saw this mess
and chose not to stay, but slip between the bricks
in his Tower of Song, the sun is still out there,
armored and gleaming. There is nothing I can say
to make it stop.

First appeared in *Asheville Poetry Review*

11

New View

What luck the sunset is something to look at—
angelic grand gesture, braggadocio
of sky. Jogger in pink socks down a tie-dye avenue.

This high up, I show it to my daughter.
I say the sun's going to bed, and the colors
are its pajamas. I say this crap, and it becomes

her *childhood*, the deep, impossible
knotting of her heart. It's hopeless, I can't help
but speak of her heart: crimson motor of meat

and stardust. Little metaphor. Mighty
tug boat. I say, you know not everything I tell you
is true. She says the sun waves goodbye,
but the moon doesn't want to.

First appeared in *American Poetry Review*

Go So You Can Come Back

Go so you can come back
says my wife, meaning go but don't linger
in frozen foods, or forget
where you parked, or chat up the cashier.
Go, certainly, because something
needs getting while the baby takes a nap,
and the snow isn't snowing,
and here are some coupons that happen
to be expiring, so go
before all the ripe produce
turns soft and stringy, and school lets out,
and a tallish boy hawking Skittles
by the entrance wins you over, and you throw him
cash, your wallet, everything for the sake
of his under-funded football team
because though you never loved football,
you love James Wright's poem about football
and solitude and those suicidally-
beautiful, galloping sons who go at it and go
because I love you, though I also love
those parmesan Popchips,
and to love is to leave
room for longing, but come back
so that we might go out together, later,
in a perpetual rotation of goings and comings
which requires nothing but patience
and faith that when we go
we remember where is home.

First appeared in *EPOCH*

Mac Barrett
nonfiction

Insufficient Fare

I can't imagine why you didn't think you'd hear from me after I nearly had a heart attack introducing myself. I appreciate your story-mindedness.

That morning, the cruelest little message, "Insufficient Fare," cost me the most crucial seconds. As the F pulled away I sat on the stairs like I was done with trains, envying the people just arriving, happily ignorant of their own poor timing. When the train did come I took my place in the door and opened my book. As usual the train leaned heavy around the elevated turn but did not fall off the track onto Smith Street. An announcement was made that a police investigation would make it necessary for the F to assume the route of an A. I wondered about the complexity of the identity of a train in such a circumstance: in what sense is the F the F once it makes A stops? Soon another announcement followed: due to a sick passenger the F train traveling on the A line would now make G stops. People began urgent conversations with one another about what to do. Everyone wanted to be helpful, or to be helped. Aggravation got the best of some and they stormed off at Bergen with the bluster of protesters. I joined the faction that planned on transferring at Hoyt-Schermerhorn Street. We had a confidence about us, a transportative swagger. We knew the meaning of these silly syllables: Hoyt–schimmer–horn. Once there, we marched up the stairs and through a stench of turpentine that made a man cover his nose with his tie, and down the other side. I walked fast to create some distance from the crowd, some room for my own identity, and, coming around a pillar, I met the eyes of a woman whose name would turn out to be You. The train came and the people crowded on. With You sitting just beyond it, my book felt like a prop, a piece of stagecraft a man named Jonathan Franzen had meticulously, obsessively designed so that I could believably pretend not to look at You. Then You got up and swept past and your eyes ran over mine and I stood there looking at the open door. The criminal and the sick person who had unknowingly conspired to bring me to this point flashed through my head. I didn't decide to walk off the train and catch up with You to say hello—I wouldn't have done that, not three stops early on a morning when I was already late—but I did let myself. To be continued over a drink. Are you free next week?

Megan Sass

lyrics

My Own Little Country

Well the world is changin' around me
It's not the way it used to be
Why should I trust reason or science
When I've got my own memory?
I'd like to have power, I'd like to have wealth
I'd like to have trophies to hang on my shelf
I'd like my leaders to offer some help
To me and to people like me

(So) I'll just stand in my corner
I'll just shout from my chair
In my own little country
In my present state
I'd rather scream now
Thank just listen and wait
It's harder to hear
So it's easier to hate
The person who screams over there
Oh how I long for the good times
Their joy and security
And though I may not have looked very closely
Things sure appeared good to me
There were no shades of gray, just white and black
Those who thought different weren't cut no slack
The world will be better when it goes back
To how I misremember it to be

I no longer feel comfort
My nation has taken a turn

My feelings are infallible
That's what the rest of you need to learn
I know I'm no longer in my element
I've a creeping suspicion I'm less relevant
I feel discomfort, and can't be content
Then I'd rather just see the world burn

Cabernet

Trivia

Celebrations

1. To prepare for her wedding ceremony and festivities, which may last seven days, a Moroccan bride bathes in *this* substance to purify herself.

Love

2. In the 1996 cinematic version of *Romeo & Juliet*, what are the titular characters dressed as when they first meet at the costume party?

Mythological Creatures

3. Most people know that a centaur is half-human half-horse, but what creature from Greek mythology is half-woman half-bird?

Awesome Women

4. *This* inspiring female artist once said, "I paint myself because I am so often alone and because I am the subject I know best." She also said, "I was born a bitch. I was born a painter."

Fashion

5. Believe it or not, upper-class British men of the 18th century pinned *this* on their hats as a memento of their lovers.

Britt Canty
fiction

Enough to Drown a Man

It was New Year's Eve, and the night belonged to Deacon. A bulb buried and lying dormant inside of him was finding its way to flower. He beamed at his girlfriend Clara, as if to say: Look at the world I can give you. Look at the men in tuxedos and women in sequined gowns. Look at the chandeliers and centerpieces lush with lavender and magnolia. Look at the way everything gleams. Clara responded with the serene, camera-ready smile she wore to please those around her. She had grown up here in Dallas, a debutante, so perhaps she was accustomed to attending such parties. Was he a fool for thinking he could impress her? The evening was just beginning, he reassured himself; he still had time to make it special somehow. He could even ask her to marry him if the perfect moment arrived. They'd only known each other for three months, but Deacon was confident he wanted her to be his wife. For the past week, his coat pocket had housed a slim jewelry box with his mother's engagement ring secured within.

Deacon took a glass of champagne. Servers were offering crystal flutes from trays so well shined their sparkling contents seemed to multiply. He took another. And another. The ache that had amassed in the back of his throat was starting to dissolve. Soon he lost track of how much he'd consumed, giving himself over to the transcendent brightness that always reminded him of Phoenix and those mornings spent at the abandoned swimming pool. He was in high school then and living with his mother in Desert Song, an apartment complex at the edge of the city. In those early hours of pink light when his mother was fast asleep on the couch, a lipstick-stained martini glass on the floor by her side, Deacon would make his quiet exit, allowing time for a detour to the pool on his way to the bus stop. He had claimed that neglected space as his own: an oasis of algae-greened water, whitewashed brick walls, and overgrown tangerine trees. Sitting cross-legged on the diving board and hovering above the half-filled basin, he imagined fresh tiles and clean water. He likened this new pool to his mind and drifted into its shimmering depths, guided by the tinkling sounds of wind chimes that decorated the units' small terraces. Such moments had made him feel expansive and connected, as if he could reach out and touch the very heart of the universe as easily as he could have dipped a toe into the water beneath him.

Deacon spotted Tim Larkin making his way toward him and Clara. Tim's hair was combed back and defined in silver-gray waves, and he was dressed in solid black, which gave audience to his polished, rattlesnake boots. Deacon now wished he'd worn something more stylish than this ill-fitting tux, a cheap rental missing its cufflinks.

"Enjoying yourselves, I hope?"

Tim lifted Clara's hand to his lips, stamping her fingers with a kiss.

"Immensely," Clara said. "Thank you."

He watched how Clara trapped Tim in her gaze—those gold-flecked brown eyes—and how she measured the seconds until looking away, at last releasing him back into what Deacon knew would feel like a colder atmosphere than before. Something caught and flashed in his chest. Had Clara grown tired of him? Was she casting about for someone new?

Tim looked pleased. "Clara, would you be so kind as to let me steal Deacon for a while?"

"Of course," she said. "He's all yours."

Deacon followed Tim as he began to describe the cache of scotch he kept in his library—dozens of bottles he'd brought back from distilleries in Islay. Once there, Deacon took a seat in the deep armchair opposite Tim, who went about clearing his desk of its stacks of legal pads and folders bound with rubber bands. Tim fixed the stub of an old cigar in the corner of his mouth, and though it was unlit, Deacon could still smell the tobacco laced with licorice and cinnamon. Without dislodging the cigar, Tim congratulated him on completing his first six months at the firm with flying colors. In spite of himself, Deacon grinned at the compliment and released his breath in a brief fit of laughter.

"Well, I'll be damned if that's not the best thing I've heard all year."

"Let's have a pop to celebrate," Tim said. "You've earned it."

Tim pulled an unlabeled bottle from his desk and poured a glass for each of them. They toasted—to many more!—and Deacon took in the rare amber, set aglow by the lamplight. With that first glass, and another, he drained deserts of smoke and forests of decay that burned and numbed, flooding him in extraordinary, womb-like warmth. He felt giddy yet centered, and wanted to find Clara, her rosewater-scented neck.

When they rejoined the party, Deacon saw her standing at one of the cocktail tables, regaling Mrs. Larkin and others who seemed spellbound. Clara had a way of moving through space like a smooth stone across water, leaving a rippling trail of light as she went. He wanted to fill the room, to be the only surface against which she could traverse, but he would have to embody oceans to satisfy her. Pressing his hand to Clara's back where her skin was exposed through a diamond-shaped keyhole, he kissed her cheek, her neck. He searched for the language to tell her about those sunrises balanced on the diving board, his lips stinging from peeling tangerines with his teeth: how he had felt contained and infinite at once. How one morning his mother—with her arm hanging off the couch at an unnatural angle and the pink light filtering her features—looked more like a forgotten doll. That was the day she never woke up. He heard the wind chimes tinkling on the terrace: suddenly a lonely and dissonant sound that gave voice to his terror. He heard glasses clinking around him.

Deacon leaned into the soft shell of Clara's ear and whispered, "Has anyone ever told you, you're astonishing." She returned his embrace, her fingers drawing a gentle line down the length of his spine. A server paused at their cocktail table to offer another round in preparation for the midnight toast. They each took a glass.

Tim let out a sharp whistle from the staircase, and they looked up to find him wielding a bottle of champagne in one hand and an ornate curved sword in the other. He announced that at midnight, which was only minutes away, he would saber the bottle. The guests clapped and cheered when he raised the blade to initiate the final ten-second countdown. Deacon held Clara's hand, squeezing it with each passing second, while the crowd sang out in unison. Even though his voice joined the others, he was starting to feel diminished and alone. He needed another scotch, but he couldn't excuse himself now. At last, the countdown climaxed, Tim's saber splitting open the bottle, which sprayed and foamed to everyone's delight. Deacon kissed Clara but found his tongue sluggish and hers timid. He tightened his grip around her waist and pulled her toward him with such force she dropped her glass. Clara gasped as it shattered against the marble floor.

Within seconds, a server was tending to the mess, and Tim was at their side. "No use crying over spilled champagne," he said. But Tim's words of consolation and the amused expression on his face only made Deacon feel more ashamed. He knelt to help the server pick up the pieces. "Always such a gentleman," he heard Tim say to Clara. "And the firm's rising star! You're one lucky lady."

Deacon looked up from the floor to find Tim putting his hand to the brim of an imaginary hat and tipping it toward Clara. He watched her smile at Tim with heartbreaking abandon until her gaze shifted back to him, and she cried out, "Deacon! You're bleeding!"

His hand was covered in blood. Deacon took the napkin the server offered and stood up in a rush.

"It's nothing. I'm fine."

"We'd better call it a night," Clara said. "Tim, thank you for your hospitality, and please give our compliments to Mrs. Larkin as well."

"The pleasure was all mine." Tim said, then turned to Deacon and clasped his shoulder. "Happy New Year, bud. Take care of yourself."

"Same to you, bud," he said in an effort to match Tim's warm tone.

As they made their way to the door, Deacon downed a final glass of champagne.

The Larkins' lawn stretched out beneath a clear sky netted in stars. Deacon's mind went to work connecting the studs of light. Rising star—he was the firm's rising star! In his constellations, Tim's library converged with the swimming pool. He wanted to drink scotch on the diving board until he expanded to hold the whole burning universe inside of him: tangerines, smoke, and radiant green. He steadied himself against Clara, who was guiding him along the moon-washed sidewalk, the nighttime air licking his skin out of a love so absolute he no longer feared anything, not even death. God-given angel, Clara. Clarity. His mother's ring.

Had you left the Larkins' party shortly after midnight, you might have seen them in the yard, their figures silhouetted by streetlight. You might have seen him on his knees in the grass, his head against her thigh as she stood cradling him. You might have wondered if he had just asked her to marry him, and then on getting closer, you might have heard his muffled sobs. Had he fallen? He seemed like the victim of a terrible accident. Or was he merely intoxicated?

They'd almost reached the car when she asked for the keys. She moved to grab them from his back pocket. He jerked away from her reach, her presence a sudden prod.

"Deacon, please—"

"It's just a cut, Clara. I can still drive."

"You're drunk, darling, and I think you need stitches."

He heard the pleading break in her voice. She looked like a little girl with his blazer draped over her shoulders. Were her eyes welling with pity for him? Taking in her god-awful sadness, he was struck by how inadequate she'd made him feel: those intimate exchanges with Tim, the broken glass and blood, and finally her refusal to accept the ring by way of some vague explanation he couldn't remember. Had she taken him for an idiot? Deacon turned and walked toward the car with imbalanced but determined swiftness. He got in and drove off, gravel shooting into the air as he spun out of the lot and left Clara standing there.

With the windows rolled down, he felt bolstered by the wind and his newfound mission: he would head downtown and check into a hotel, where there would be a bar and a pool—one with clean, shimmering water.

His finger was throbbing, and the steering wheel had turned sticky with blood. He could turn back, make amends with Clara, and go to the hospital for stitches. But turning back seemed impossible; the night had fallen away like scenery from the window of a train as he found himself inside a world of his own, hurtling toward something he couldn't yet name. Besides, she never knew. His mother. Clara. She didn't understand that he was brimming with love for her—it was enough to drown a man. As the traffic light ahead turned red, Deacon accelerated. He could see the city skyline emerging in the distance, the tallest building outlined in neon green.

First appeared in *Bookanista*

Jenny Williamson
poetry

Night Reach

I don't know why I came out here. This place is
the inside of all tombs; a horizon collapsed on itself,
black as world's end. The sea is no color

I recognize. There are mysteries here;
they all know my name. I am right
to be afraid.

I came here
I suppose to hear your voice again. Everyone knows there are ghosts
on the beach at night; no one

can give me what I need. I am a comet unraveling,
bright smear against the dark; no one can touch me. I miss
being touched.

If I stand here long enough, there will be
a wave big enough to bury me.
We all need to believe

in something. You have no idea how far I've come
since you left me. You
have no idea.

About a Body

Like everything else I have done,
there came a time when it stopped
being easy.

Nothing else ever changes. There is still the same woman
leaning out of every billboard. We love her most
for the places she is least.

Still. I wanted to be as she is. I wanted to look
like I feel, which is to say
like a glider. Streamlined aerodynamo; the kind of woman

who uses each part of the animal.
The kind who looks like hunger would
if it walked; clean atmosphere

between my thighs. Blameless body bends itself
to survival. I pound my softness into dirt; consign my excess
to the dead. The thing I want most is to see

how close I can come. When I am old and unbeautiful
I shall walk this city like a cursed wind.
I will raise my arms to the billboard woman; together

we will tear down all you have wrought. See;
come and see what you've done to us. Tell me
who will know me then. Who will love me now.

Christie Grotheim
nonfiction

A Second Round of Firsts

It occurred to me recently that I am at a stage of life in which I am once again experiencing a series of unprecedented firsts. And these are not skydiving out of an airplane, backpacking across India, mind-expanding kinds of firsts. Rather, they are jaw dropping, horrifying firsts, where the only thing I'm discovering is a new awareness of my own inherent descent.

As the oldest of four children in my family, I was the first to experience a plethora of well-documented firsts: first tooth, first steps, first day or kindergarten, first to ride a bike. I remember how empowering each accomplishment felt, like I was a pioneer at the forefront of achievement— in my household at least. Each triumph was a thrill. I found I could surpass expectations just by developing normally, with everyday milestones inducing enthusiastic reactions of affirmation and applause.

In fact, I sometimes feel my parents showered me with too much attention and encouragement early on that could not be sustained throughout adulthood. No one was there to cheer me on when I recently baked my first quiche or when I completed my first bathroom grout cleaning. Sometimes I tell my husband, Niklas, my accomplishments when he comes home from work expecting accolades—only to be met with a moderate reaction.

By the time you reach forty, nobody pats you on the back; in fact, people *expect* you to have your shit together. And not just in terms of household chores. Having a successful career is no longer celebrated. Now it's a basic necessity to compensate for the fact that the looks you used to rely on are fading. Mentally you are expected to be at your pinnacle, while physically things begin to plummet, leading you into a second round of frightening firsts.

There was the first gray hair, an expected cliché and not that upsetting, followed by a few more strands mostly hidden deep in my curly helmet of dark hair. A far worse first was spotting a gray pubic hair, a curly strand as white as Santa's beard, and almost as long, growing in my beautiful dark bush. I was mortified. Blindsided. It had never crossed my mind that this could happen. Or if it did, I expected it wouldn't be until I was wearing an adult diaper and too far gone to care, not to a hot young thing like myself wearing a thong from Victoria's Secret. And this was one secret Victoria had damn well better keep! I grabbed onto the silver strand and pulled it out like a weed, eradicating it while writhing in pain.

Another shocker was a couple of years ago, on a beautiful spring day when I could finally leave the house in short sleeves, the sun warming me all over. Unfortunately the beams also lit up several spots on my forearms, glowing as bright as stars. An entire constellation formed a few days later. The dots stood out on my fair skin like a disease. What the heck *are* those? I kept asking my husband. Do you *see* those? Oh yeah, I see them, he said, not even reaching for his glasses. But it didn't take a dermatologist to confirm what I suspected deep down—that they were age spots. I've learned since then that by mid-summer the white specks will tan if I spend weeks in the sun without sunblock, further damaging the dying splotches of skin.

Things appear; things disappear. There was the first time I realized why some old ladies draw on eyebrows, and it was not that they were aging cabaret dancers like I had always assumed. I noticed that around the age of forty the brows begin to thin. I saw it on my friends, I saw it in the mirror, and I longed for my bushy-eyed high school self, when I was fighting a unibrow. At least that could be divided and conquered. Skimpy brows are especially troubling in these times with the ultra-bold, artificially-angled sci-fi styles the young kids are wearing. While I personally think it looks ridiculous, I see now the statement they are making: they're announcing to the world that they do it simply because they *can*.

Some things die; others grow. Recently I spotted a stray darker hair on my upper lip. I wanted to nip this full on future mustache in the bud, but didn't know how to deal with it. Did women of a certain age use laser surgery, bleach, or a hair removal product? I said fuck it and decided to pluck it. To my horror a tiny droplet of blood appeared. But no matter how much blood must be shed I will continue tweeze it until I hopefully kill the follicle.

Skin cells themselves continue to split and to sprout—and in all the wrong places. I'll never forget the first time I found a skin tag in my left armpit, small but stubborn. For those of you who have yet to produce one, a skin tag is like a mole without color, a benign growth, flaccid and floppy while somehow holding on firm. Wanting to save myself a trip to the doctor, I asked Niklas to remove it with an exacto knife. We were off to Europe the very next day, and I didn't want to take the little bugger along for the ride. We numbed the area well with an ice cube, but I could still feel him sawing back and forth on the thing with all his might. He stopped mid-surgery to change the blade, as a sort of central tendril held on tight. As traumatic as it was for both of us, the operation was a success.

A couple of years ago I noticed I looked mad in all my Facebook pictures when in fact I was not. Zooming in to look more closely, I saw that it was because of the deep creases between my brows. Unfortunately I realized that this tense scowl was now my new resting face. I've gotten used to it; you kind of have to grow into yourself, I've found. And in fact you are forced to get used to yourself again and again and again.

And that was nothing compared to the first time I looked in the mirror and saw that my mouth had dropped. I knew boys' balls dropped, but I had no idea women's mouths dropped. Or at least mine did, giving in to gravity around the edges, making me look not like my mother but my father, jowls like a hound dog. This was recent and tears fell down my sagging cheeks when I stared at my reflection, shocked at the familiar stranger I saw. It was that sudden. When you're young you assume aging will be gradual, and when you put all of the changes together it is indeed a slow but steady decline, yet the individual atrocities literally happen overnight.

While drinking my coffee, depressed, I thought about something I'd seen in the subway some time ago. A woman, probably ten years my senior, looked at me with a close-lipped smile, not an unpleasant expression, yet still I kept questioning whether she some kind of whackjob. But she was well-dressed and didn't look crazy, and she aimed her soft smile at others as they got on, maintaining the expression throughout the ride.

And just then it hit me: she was holding up her face. Fighting the heavy weight of gravity by tilting her lips skyward. And I realized that my mom wears that same expression, and my grandma had worn it before her. I suddenly understood that it's the poor man's—or rather the stoic woman's—alternative to plastic surgery. And I empathized with all the cat-women of the world.

The ironic thing is, even with all these heinous changes, I wouldn't want to be in my twenties again, or even in my thirties. I'm more comfortable in my own skin now, no matter that it's losing its elasticity. I like the crow's feet curling up around my eyes, the hint of an easy, knowing smile. I like my overall physique in that it's strong, enduring. No longer taking my health for granted, I revel in it, in being active, and in just being.

Lately I'm learning to quiet down and listen to my gut—and really feel with my senses. It's like I'm just now getting to know myself even after living with myself all these years. I'm finally understanding what makes me happy, what makes me tick.

And there are still fabulous firsts: like being in love with a life partner, experiencing unconditional love that grows deeper. Like the gray pube, I didn't know this would exist for me.

Like exploring the ruins of Tulum with this man, wandering hand in hand in silence. Like being able to be still and focused enough to write a novel. Or standing next to a hot air balloon breathing fire at night, wild colors lit up from the inside, enjoying its heat while envisioning myself inside it.

And there are the moments that are seconds or thirds but feel like firsts because I've finally taken the time to notice, like breathing in the smell of soil during a quiet walk in the woods alone or like savoring the taste of an heirloom tomato sprinkled with sea salt.

I expect more exciting firsts in the second half of this journey. I *will* ride in a hot air balloon. I *will* publish that novel. And I *will* embrace life and myself with a tight close-lipped smile, a smile that not only holds up my face but reflects my secret inner self, my contentment.

Adam Blotner
lyrics

Interesting Girl

She wears t-shirts in the rain
She only laughs on Wednesdays
She tells me that herself is not who she wants to be now

She likes to buy in bulk
She drinks water from the toilet
She tells me it's two thirty when it's really a quarter to three now

She's scared to use the remote
In summer she wears a coat

The girl is so ironic, it's like everything she does is opposite
from the way that a normal person would do things, isn't that
interesting?

And the way I know she loves me, is that she tells me that she loves me
So I'm telling the whole world I'm in love with an interesting girl

Do do do do do...

She wears a wedding dress to sleep
She thinks the alphabet's just a kind of soup
She only likes to tap dance if she's wearing Reeboks

She's a vegetarian
But she goes hunting every weekend
She don't believe in God but she believes in Ewoks

She likes her soup on a plate

She doesn't like to wait

The girl is so ironic, it's like everything she does is opposite
from the way that a normal person would do things, isn't that
interesting?

And the way I know she loves me, is that she tells me that she loves me
So I'm telling the whole world I'm in love with an interesting girl

Do do do do do...

Dirty Martini

Trivia

Sex

1. In ancient Egypt, women wore *this* if they were especially skilled at performing oral sex.

The Supernatural

2. What type of supernatural being appears in dreams to seduce men and feed off their sexual energy?

Name that Song

3. Written by Lenny Kravitz and Ingrid Chavez, *this* song caused worldwide controversy after its music video depicted images of S&M, voyeurism, and bisexuality.

Psychology

4. In *this* stage of Freudian psychosexual development, children first become aware of their genitalia, learn the physical differences between male and female bodies, and experience the Oedipus or Electra complex.

Inventions and Innovations

5. In 16th-century Italy, a man named Gabriele Falloppio claimed to have invented *this* object, made from linen sheaths soaked in a chemical solution and held onto the body with ribbon, though they'd also been used years earlier in Asia, made then of lamb intestines and other animal parts.

Nancy Hightower
fiction

Hip Hugger

It was Jane's second Tinder texting marathon with a thirty-something entrepreneur. Their messages were ten words or less, many of which, between autofilling and autocorrection, Jane has little to no control over. She once tried to tell a man she was on her way to teach a class and had no time for texting, but that they should grab drinks at the Rubin Museum later. It came out on the other side of the autocorrect gateway as *no time for sexting, let's get drinks at the Ruin Museum.* Apparently that's where all the naughty sexting girls meet up.

Said boy was confused but intrigued, until Jane corrected the mistake. She considered including some kind of warning in her Tinder profile along the lines of *artistic intellectual with enormous thumbs,* but she worried what kind of man that might attract. This particular hipster liked to begin his chats with a simple *hey* and often ended with *are you wearing panties?* While a saucy message was appreciated now and then, Jane did not have the heart to tell him on this particular day that she was wearing plain black Hanes, sweatpants, and horn-rimmed glasses while grading a stack of essays. She both did and didn't want to set the record straight that it was actually inconsequential whether or not she was wearing panties since there is always, according to Plato, the Intangible Form of Pantyness, the Panty that is perfect and unchanging regardless of whether any woman was wearing them. Her Tinder match did not understand that having been asked the question so many times on so many different occasions Jane had become one with the Panty. She was the Panty. Jane was close to texting this philosophical freebasing in a mad flurry of messages but then reconsidered and simply replied, *maybe.*

Ha ha, he wrote back, *don't know you know? Maybe you should check.*

Jane sighed. Not every man she met online was a panty man. One took her on a seven-hour date where he never once asked her about panties, thongs, or thigh highs, but he did inquire about her dating history, education, and family dynamics. He looked slightly indignant when she confessed the lack of vegetables in her diet. Perhaps it would have softened the blow if she had lied and said she didn't do underwear, either. He didn't run away in horror at the revelation, but he did order an artichoke heart for them to share and later finished the untouched salad on her plate when she said she was full, all the while reminding Jane how healthy eating could be fun.

That experience made Jane wary to reveal personal information very often, but now, with her hipster eagerly waiting for confirmation, she had a choice. If she said *why yes, I am wearing panties*, he would ask what kind, and then Jane would have to confess that she didn't get all of her laundry done, that what she had on were considered second-rate panties, not period panties or workout panties. In fact, these were riding up a bit, and not in that sexy, Victoria's Secret Cheekini kind of way. If she said no, he would want to take the conversation to another level that Jane, with her clumsy thumbs and an autocorrect which bordered on S&M, could participate in without kicking ducks or locking up tots.

Jane hesitated, wanting to explore this metafictional moment where it didn't matter whether she was actually wearing panties, that Schrodinger's cat has nothing on the state of her lingerie since Jane was merely appropriating the panty as a theoretical construct, the color of which was to be determined in a matter of seconds, but, as part of the dating/sexting social contract theory, should have been red or black. To bring in polka dots, ice cream cones, palm trees or a host of other designs that might be spotted on her second rate buy-three-for-fifteen-dollar collection would be in strict violation of the semantic paradigm.

By now the hipster had sent several questions marks and was most likely beginning to doubt Jane's sanity since it was taking this long to decide whether or not she was wearing underwear. Jane glanced at the stack of ungraded papers she would soon attack with a bright red pen (prompting her to contemplate why she had red pens as opposed to red panties, but now was not the time). She finally wrote back in a flurry of words: *how do you feel about red stripes?*

But Jane's texts were warped by a Freudian matrix she could never escape. She realized autofill had morphed what she had thought was a candy cane metaphor into "red strikes," as if any romantic encounter with her bordered on a planned military operation.

I'm in, he responded.

She was out.

A version of this story first appeared in *Queen Mob's Teahouse*

Jordana Frankel
poetry

In the beginning, God is born with a scream

No different than the rest of us, she aches
into being: an infinite gasp, a howl past the lip
of some careening black hole. An imagining of awe.

If she must, she will chew off her leg to escape...

"I am the devourer, I will not be devoured,"
she remembers, and turns on the lights.
They spring forth from nothing, easy as an idea.

Through a window in the Paris Hotel, a shadowy man
trains his lens on her naked breasts. His cock is hard.
"I am looking at God," he realizes, withering.

This is how She enters the world...

If Love is light then Longing is its shadow,
and she recalls the Void with fondness:
its relentless ripping of dreams, its comfortable demise.

Midday, God brushes stars from her burning hair,
anoints her night black skin with oils.
"I conceived of myself in darkness," she whispers, awestruck.
"But I am something new now and cannot go back, only forth."

She fucks herself in the bathtub then, an act of disgusted reclamation.
Under her finger, her clitoris pulses like a sine wave:
the first harmonic. High on the invention of music, collisions of color

quake between her kneecaps: afterbirth red, revolution yellow.

She composes spectrums, a chorus of angels
in the quantum thrum of electrons.
No longer does she long for Herself.
Her climax *is* the extravagant gesture.
The very stuff of creation.

"Come in," she says to the knock on the door.
In the hallway, lamplight holds You like a halo.
She has fucked You into being and now You are here too,
aching your own way from the darkness.
You shudder.

"Is it still cold there?" she asks. Her voice is wistful.
You do not answer. You undress. In the bathtub,
in the shadow of Her longing, You sing the second song.

Simi Toledano
nonfiction

Susan in Paris

On the train from De Gaulle Airport to Paris city center, I started feeling nervous and excited to see Susan again. It was August 2012 and I had just completed a six-week backpacking trip through Europe, culminating in a fifteen-hour overnight layover in Paris with a former lover who had arranged for us to meet at a hotel two blocks from the Eiffel Tower. The sexy rendezvous would be the cherry on top of a summer defined by travel, friendship, and personal growth, and all I wanted was to savor its sweetness.

As I walked from the train station to the Renaissance Paris Le Parc Trocadero Hotel, I noticed that the Eiffel Tower was dark. Rather than dazzling in the night sky like a beacon of joy, it loomed like a grand and mysterious watchtower. The city of light turns its lights off in August, when tourism is slow and Parisians flee the city for the beaches. The dark, empty streets created a peaceful atmosphere that felt at once comforting and discomforting, as if the Great Mystery was sizing me up. It was midnight when I arrived at the hotel. My entrance turned the heads of the concierge and they watched as I floated toward the courtyard.

I'd met Susan six months earlier at a potluck lunch in New Orleans, where we both lived at the time. I was immediately attracted to her androgyny and her self-defined unicorn energy—playful and confident. She had a curly blond mane, which I found wildly intimidating, and an impish smirk, which melted my heart and my boundaries. The day I met her was also the day we first hooked up, which was also the day she casually pulled out a huge blue dildo from her backpack. That night, Susan sent me to new heights of pleasure and all I wanted was more.

When we first met, Susan told me she wasn't looking for a connection because she had just gotten out of a serious relationship. I pretended that I wasn't either and continued to pursue her until she moved to London that April for a job. I was a spellbound idiot, bedazzled by her unicorn glitter,

41

flirtatious one-word texts, our amazing sexual chemistry, and that smirk. Despite my deep dissatisfaction, however, I continued to seek love and affection from her, an emotionally unavailable hybrid human being/mythical creature. You could say I was dick whipped by her blue dildo.

Stepping outdoors into a pixie lit courtyard, I saw Susan sitting with a leg propped up on a coffee table. She was wearing a multicolored, paisley windbreaker with black jeans, and that smile. On the table was a plate with a half-eaten ham sandwich and an open bottle of Rosé. She looked me up and down. I was wearing all-black—t-shirt, mini skirt, and leggings—with white Keds, feeling sexy and confident. Already swooning, I made a deal with the Great Mystery: Oh, you are SO on.

Susan said I looked good. "I feel good!" I retorted. Her mane had become a shaggy mop top, and her mood was melancholy. For the first time I noticed that she was actually smaller than me. I had classified her as a majestic bike-riding unicorn, and now she was just a person, one that I didn't know very well. I felt disappointed by my own expectations but decided to lie and compliment her ugly jacket. I didn't want her to be disappointed too.

Susan told me she was having a hard time in London. She was feeling lonely without a close group of friends. I felt a pang in my gut. *Is she using me for sex because she's lonely? Does she even care about me? No, forget that. She got the hotel room. Don't upset her, don't rock the boat.* I reasoned that she wouldn't use me because in our correspondence leading up to this night I had divulged my feelings for her. I'd said I was interested in connection and wouldn't make an effort to meet her unless she was willing to explore that with me. I blindly trusted her to be careful with my heart.

Sitting with her in the courtyard, I began to feel uncomfortable and heard a small voice say *not all that glitters is gold.* But in an effort to keep Susan feeling comfortable I buried my intuition and we ascended to our room on the tenth floor. We started undressing the minute we opened the door. I was shocked to see Susan wearing lacy underwear with bows. "Your underwear is so girly!" I said.

"Surprise!" she exclaimed, as she threw me down on the bed.

Though she didn't have her blue dildo, our chemistry in Paris, the city of love, had reignited the passion and obsession I thought I had outgrown. That night Susan sent me into yet another dimension of pleasure, the world never quite feeling the same in its aftermath.

"Let's roll a spliff and go for a walk." She motioned toward the window overlooking the street. It was 2am and we were lying in bed. My mind was still swirling from our lovemaking and, in a semi-dream state, I accepted her invitation. I got dressed, grabbed my clutch, and we exited the hotel into the dark Paris night.

We smoked as we walked to the Eiffel Tower and lay down in the shadow of its towering magnificence. Susan took hold of my hand and I melted into her eyes. I was feeling high on life and marijuana.

"In the world of possibility," I whispered, "what could we do right now?"

"We could get some orange juice," she suggested.

We laughed and began to search for orange juice. Surprisingly, at 3am, there was an open newsstand. I reached for my clutch to pay for Susan's orange juice only to feel air. A flash of fear jolted my heart. Where was my clutch? I didn't have my clutch. I didn't have my clutch that had my passport, phone, and credit card in it. Where was it? I told Susan my clutch was missing, and felt my center crumble.

"I want to cry," I said, giving into the despair.

"Don't cry," she pleaded. Despite needing an emotional release, my need to please was stronger. I looked up at the Eiffel Tower, beholding my fear and despair, and swallowed my tears. As we retraced our steps I wondered if Susan had stolen my clutch as a prank. But I didn't ask her, and we didn't find the clutch.

We got back to the hotel and I went straight to the concierge. I knew I was going to have to do this alone. I couldn't break down and I couldn't get what I needed from Susan, which was to be told that I am strong and resilient and that she was going to help me through this catastrophe. In that moment it became clear that she was a stranger who was creating chaos in my life. What I needed was to set some boundaries and prioritize myself. I knew the end of this story.

My tension lifted at that moment and I laughed. I knew the end of this story! I knew this would end with me back in the U.S. I was going to get myself home by any means necessary. I wondered how often the concierge saw a character like me: frazzled traveler who loses their passport the night before their flight home because of an earth-shattering orgasm in the most romantic city in the world. I wanted to be an elegant and sophisticated woman who had fun and emotionally detached Parisian love affairs. Though, at twenty-four years old, I was still susceptible to being thrown off balance by a good orgasm. Hell, I'm still susceptible. It's a lifelong condition.

The U.S. Embassy would be open for emergency passport services between 8:30am and10:30am the next day, and would cost €115. I looked over at Susan, who had dozed off, and realized that I would need to ask her for money. I felt embarrassed for ruining the evening and needing to ask for help. I woke her up and, on our way back to the room, she offered to lend me as much money as I needed. I squeezed her with gratitude.

We were in bed by 4am and set the alarm for 7:30. My body was pumping with adrenaline and kept reviewing the timetable in my mind. I just needed to be on my way to De Gaulle airport by 11:30am for my 1:30pm flight. *I know the end of this story,* I said to myself. And I drifted off into a half-sleep.

We arrived at the U.S. Embassy at 8:30. Susan gave me her credit card and pin number and we departed. Waiting in line for security, I was told that I needed to provide a photo for my emergency passport before getting an appointment. They had a photo booth in the foyer for seven Euro. I walked ten minutes to the nearest ATM and took out enough money for the passport photo, returning only to find that they would only accept cash for the emergency passport as well. Feeling exasperated and feral, I rushed to the ATM once more to take out 200 Euro. By 9am, I had gotten through security with my emergency passport photo.

During my meeting with the ambassador, I became the charming and confident woman who got swept off her feet in Paris. I told the male ambassador that I'd lost my purse, and my mind, because of love. "How silly I am," I lowered my eyes in faux embarrassment, "you must see a lot of people like me." I giggled softly and looked pleadingly into his eyes. He blushed and promised I'd get an emergency passport that day. Indeed, by 10:15am I exited the embassy with a passport in my purse, feeling relieved and desperate to go home.

I found Susan outside, resting on a grassy knoll under the soft mid-morning sun. I had time to spare so we decided to get coffee. We noted how the streets were empty and most of the cafés and restaurants closed. It felt like we were walking through a chic ghost city. "That's Paris in August," a passerby told us as we inquired about an open café nearby.

At 11:20am, after our coffee and croissants, Susan and I went underground to the Chatelet train station for our departure and the next leg of my journey home. She reminded me exactly what I needed to do: take the RER B train to Charles De Gaulle Airport. It would take forty-five minutes. She looked me in the eyes and suddenly pulled me close for a passionate farewell kiss. She just as soon disappeared, leaving my puckered lips hovering in the air. Dumbstruck, I stared at the empty space in front of me until I heard "De Gaulle" in an overhead announcement and snapped back to the physical world. Feeling newly empowered and still quite disoriented from that kiss, I got on the next train that pulled into the station, certain I was on my way home.

I was not on my way home. It turned out I had gone fifteen minutes in the complete opposite direction of the airport. In a state that can only be described as "frantically calm," I got off the train and on the next one to Chatelet, where I got on the correct train to the airport. I arrived just in time to see my flight take off without me.

I felt like a victim of the Great Mystery and her antics. But there was no time for self-pity; I needed to act. I knew the end of this story, I just didn't know *how* I was going to get there. After hours of waiting in lines and being handed off between Delta and Air France customer service and ticketing agents, bumming cigarettes from strangers, and *not* crying, I finally met George, a Delta ticketing agent who found me a ticket on a flight leaving at 1:30pm the next day. "It will just cost you €200 for the transferal fee," he said.

"I don't think you understand," my heart finally broke and I began to cry, "I have €20 to my name right now. My credit card was stolen. I have been traveling for six weeks and I just missed my flight home. Please, I just want to go home."

George looked at me with compassion and began typing furiously. He stared at the screen with a furrowed brow for about a minute and finally spoke in a hushed tone. "I am going to print you a ticket for this flight tomorrow but you must tell the Air France agents that you bought it in the airport. My job relies on it."

My heart flooded with gratitude and spilled over with fresh tears. "Your act of kindness is literally my ticket home and I don't know how to thank you enough," I gushed to him. He blushed and handed me my ticket. I was one step closer to the end of the story.

I spent the next twenty hours sleeping in the airport and to this day my flight to Philadelphia is a blur. The end of the story, though, is that I arrived home safely. My luggage arrived two weeks later.

Looking back on the crazy night with Susan, I learned something about myself. I see just how much power I gave her, and how powerless I felt around her. I gave her that power because she could make me come. I gave her power by prioritizing her comfort over my emotional needs, and the smaller I tried to make myself the bigger my problems became. I believe the Great Mystery responded to my personal dismissal of my intuition by creating enough chaos to wake me up and tell me: this is what happens when you don't express your emotions and needs. People don't owe me their emotional care and I don't owe people their expectation of sex.

Months later I wrote Susan an email to express to her that while I had fun that night, I also felt used. She never responded. I guess my gut was right in the end—she didn't care about my feelings. Susan's unicorn glitter may have put a spell on me, but Paris in August taught me that indeed not all that glitters is gold, and I deserve gold.

Jessica Delfino
lyrics

A Sweet Fucking Word

I love the word fuck, it's a great fucking word
If you live in this world, it's a word that you've heard
And it gets so much flack, the word fuck, but you see,
If it weren't for fuck, there would be no you or me

Because fuck is the fire that excites us and joins us
Not intercourse, not copulation or coitus
Your parents, they met once and with some odd luck
Your dad wooed your mom so well that they did fuck

So now here is a chance just to scream it out loud
Don't worry that your parents might not be proud
For there was a time when they two screamed it too
And screamed so darn loud they created a you

So come on, you all, without further ado
Let's all yell out fuck—on my count of two

One, two, Fuck!
That was quite nice so let's try it again
One, two, Fuck!
Not sure if I heard you, let's have a refrain,
One, two, Fuck!
It's a beautiful word with a lovely bouquet
One, two, Fuck!
Please take it with you and use it today!

Now if you're in pain or you're feeling upset,
Say "fuck" and it takes your mind off it, I bet

48

But I most love to utter the word when all's well!
When I bite a sandwich and I say, Fuck, that's swell!

It offers some calm when life tells you to stick it,
When you miss your train or get a parking ticket
It even brings comfort during moments of grief
Just say the word fuck, and I promise relief

When you hammer your thumb or your ball gets a knee
When a spider bites or you sit in subway pee
It's a cheerful cure all for when life is a schmuck
Just look to the sky and cry out the word "fuck!"

Yes, it's real, it's powerful and it's a joy
Women can use it too, it's not just for boys
Be proud of the language, you didn't create it
But it's your right to use it, there's no need to hate it

One, two, Fuck!
That was fine but I bet you can do better
One, two, Fuck!
I beseech you to use it this week in a letter
One, two, Fuck!
Don't you already feel the weight of life lift?
One, two, Fuck!
That's my present to you, promise me you'll regift

It would be my mating call, were I a bird
Be brave and say fuck more—it's fun and absurd
The loveliest lyric you rarely have heard
I love the word fuck, it's a sweet fucking word

Bloody Mary

Trivia

Literary Villains

1. Most villains have a fatal weakness; for *this* non-human character, that involves a fear of fire.

Banned Books

2. *This* middle-grade novel features a scene in which a newborn baby is injected with lethal poison and thrown down a trash chute because he's a twin.

John Lennon

3. Before Capitol Records replaced it with a much safer image, which album cover depicted The Beatles surrounded by meat and decapitated baby dolls?

Fairy Tales

4. On the surface, *this* fairy tale warns children not to speak to strangers, but it also symbolizes a girl's sexual awakening and the start of her menstrual cycle. In one early version of the tale, the girl takes off her clothes and climbs into bed with a predatory male, who promptly kills her.

Teen Angst

5. In both the film and novel, Carrie goes on a psychokinetic rampage at her school prom after *this* is dumped all over her. Be specific!

Amy Dupcak
poetry

Sold!

I just learned that Kurt's sweater—
the one he wore playing Bowie,
Vaselines, that old Leadbelly
tune that goes back further than
Leadbelly—the one made of green mohair,
limp orchids & lithium—the one that reeks of
mothballs, antacids, sweat from the shakes—
the one scarred with cigarette burns, stains, one
missing button like an animal's eye—the one
that couldn't warm his bones, even after
three cups of tea—the one he wore exactly
twenty-six years ago, only four months before
swallowing too many Rohypnol,
only five months before burning out
like a star—sold at auction this week for
three-hundred thirty-four grand.
I wonder where the winner will keep
this new treasure—next to their own sweaters?
On a mannequin with angel wings? Maybe
they're lying in bed with it now, running
their palms across its vintage skin,
holding the coarse fabric close enough
to hear the echoes of a cello & a dopesick voice
wondering where you slept, wondering
who sold you the world & what
gave you the right to own it.

Godspeed

If these trees could talk,
they'd tell you that, of all
winged things, red sparrows
have the worst neuroses,
but at least they're kind. Not like
those blueneck grackles whose
haughty laughs crack the branches
they colonize; might as well
have bony hands to wield forest
swords, cause explosions
in the sky. If these trees could reach
any higher, they're write codes
in the clouds, warn latecomers seeking
sanctuary, or call Isis long distance.
When the true beasts come,
that ancient goddess won't protect,
might say godspeed! and hope
for the best, admitting defeat
without any insurrection—those days
are gone. The trees don't know it,
but god is an astronaut, not some
apex, or deity, or world to ponder
alone in the dark. god climbs
the stratosphere on swells
of carbon breath, claiming heaven
for himself, and he doesn't
need wings. Those things
are for the living, mere beings
that bottleneck and can't help reaching
for a higher consciousness,
much to their demise. What are trees
but future holograms, tools for another

day, vessels of innovation? This forest,
Isis knows, will never become
some silver Mt. Zion, never
be home to anything
that doesn't intend to die.

Band names intentionally referenced in this poem: If These Trees Could Talk, Red
Sparowes, Neurosis, Blueneck, Forest Swords, Explosions in the Sky, Codes in the
Clouds, Isis, Long Distance Calling, Godspeed You! Black Emperor, God is an
Astronaut, Future Holograms, Tool, Silver Mt. Zion.

Scott Alexander Hess
fiction

novel excerpt from
The Root of Everything

Richard, Brownsville, 1905

The sky had gone a soft grey at dusk, promising snow and casting the
woodlands with a gentle hush. The evening wind was high-pitched and
increasingly strong. It would dip below zero soon. The men were happy to
end their day. Some were getting to town; others had bottles and would
gather, sharing stories in the barracks. It was Christmas Eve.

Richard and Rolf huddled near the pit fire. They had agreed to work
late for extra pay.

"Get on," yelled Carney. "It's Christmas, ye' greedy fucks."

The brothers had saved nearly enough money for a two-day trip to the
St. Louis World's Fair before it ended. This extra work would cinch it. Rolf
was overjoyed.

Carney ambled toward the fire. He was well liked, as was Rolf. Richard
did not join the men in card games or drinking songs and did not linger
talking after hours. He was respected, but not liked. Richard also was not
as adept at picking up English.

"Hey," Rolf said.

Carney offered Rolf a slug from a bottle nestled under his coat. Richard
lifted a hand in protest, catching his younger brother's eye. They had to
tackle the demon tree before nightfall, the one mighty cedar that hadn't
been cut down that day as planned. Mr. Herron hated to be off schedule.

"Merry Christmas," Carney said, slapping Richard on the back.

"You both come to my bunk when you're done destroying that tree.
You can tell me all about what you lugs did on Christmas back in Germany,
and what you're gonna see first when you get to the fair," Carney said. "See
ya later Rolf."

The men sang as they drifted into darkness, away from the fire's light.
Richard looked up at the sky as it started to snow. It did not begin slowly,

rather rushed forth with a mighty burst, like a thread had snapped on a high up casing releasing thousands of snowflakes. The wind sang high and hard. He thought of last Christmas back home, eating his mother's Christmas Strudel. Through the increasing wall of snow came Mr. Herron.

"You still think you can do this?" he said.

Drawing closer to the fire, his black hair dusted white with snow, he yelled in German to them.

"*Kannst du in diesem sturm arbeiten?*"

"Yes," Richard said.

Richard slapped Rolf on the shoulder and drew him away before Mr. Herron changed his mind. They moved toward the eight foot two-man saw and the demon tree. Richard had great faith in their combined strength and the grace of Christmas. He was sure they could get through this tree before the pitch-black hit, or the snow started to pile too high and drift. The snow was turning in on itself, blowing in a chaotic dance, wild and untamed with a newly fearsome wind. He motioned to his brother.

The earlier sound of men singing was completely blighted by the wind, the hollering had stopped and the only light was the one burning in the cabin where Herron lived. They reached the tree as the first bits of hail smacked their cheeks. Richard yelled to Rolf and they started.

They each gripped their side of the long powerful saw and set into the oak end to end. They could barely see one another through the growing storm, but the saw's teeth clenched, their arms strained, those long jaws of metal bit into the tree, moving slowly and surely.

"*Stetig!*" Richard yelled, reminding Rolf to keep it steady and smooth.

They found a rhythm, the dance in twos, a movement which would continue with gentle force, moving through the beastly thing, severing its life, pulsing into it bit by bit.

There was in the howling wind the high cry of a powerful winged creature, *a crested flycatcher* Richard thought as he moved in time with his brother. The hail picked up, pelting his head, tapping his frozen cheeks but he kept on.

He looked across at Rolf just for a moment, but in that moment the teeth caught a snag, some uneven tear in the inner guts of the tree, a reckless twist. As the saw connected and was jolted by the flaw, the thing snapped out of their hands, shivered and bellowed with the wind, yanking out of the innards of the tree and vibrating forth into the gray and icy wilderness. Richard was thrown back, and he thought *that is the hand of God.* But as he stood up, as the hail increased, slashing at him, he saw his brother in a heap, where the wild and shaking saw had left him, cut nearly in half.

Kyle Pritz
poetry

Seasons

It was the year each season
held their own seasons
and it rained until it could no longer.
A clear path led out into
the headlands. And I ran until
I could no longer. I was carried
staccato by the winds to the breech
like the weight of the salt in the air.
I am the storm that's closing in;
I am the one, wobbling—now
the object of the hunter—on all fours, gaping
into the mirrors of the garden.
I held the rivers in my hand to see
my face. I held your breath with mine.
A hunter so graceful at being hunted
turns the silent game into a walk of mirrors,
so fine it's hard to hear the crescendo
of shatters, or to taste the glass I'm eating.
My dogged reflection does not lie like I do:
I was a hunter until I had to hunt;
a lover until I had to love;
a taker until I was nothing left.
I am blown, dust of glass,
and you are laced with me until you stop to bleed.

Reasons for Moving

Everything is fine here at the bottom
of this breath.

I skip a glance across the surface
of the sound.

I see the peach of cataclysm set on the horizon
of this world.

If anybody's asking, my body's drawing breath
until it's time,

and faith is nothing but the plume of burning wilderness
doused with industry

and fossil fuels; drenched not knowing why I reek
powerless.

All over, I see a thousand plastered faces, each one
loads a magazine to its teeth,

each one, the wrong chatroom away from bringing
what's in the trunk to the little league game,

the parking lot, the cafeteria. I'm getting back to the
bottom of everything,

it feels like so good to know I can still breathe.
I can choose how

deep, how slow I make the wind go.
I can make

the wind say yes or no and it feels like so good to move
around all this

involuntariness like air—I'm going from burning, everything
burning down, to

making out the best of what I don't know
comes next—looped inside the same tune

until I break or I break
it. Sometimes that's all there is to do.

Brian Birnbaum
fiction

novel excerpt from
Emerald City

There's Peter Fosch. He blends into the family room—a common area for people who happen to share his DNA. The dented empties. A hamper that threw up its clothes. TV dinners congealing over their stink. This is where he's learned about uncleanliness, ungodliness, being close to nothing.

He pulls knees to stomach and sniffs up some drip, his eyes following father, who hunches center stage, breath ragged, broken by pulls off the fifth he chokes at the neck, belaboring unintelligible accusations at his wife, whose wayward finger thrusts into his retina.

"CUNT," he bellows, hand over eye. He knocks into the TV and up the stairs.

His mother staggers, wet coins of vodka dappling the front of her shirt. She looms. "Fuck're you lookin at?" she asks Peter, and her eyes, like lolling glass, make the question seem literal. "You ain't shit. I'll cut yer gas line you look'me."

She staggers off.

There's Kaleigh Fosch, the next day, returning home from a friend's house. She's wearing bell bottom jeans and a white peplum blouse, flowery lace at the cuffs. Garments beyond her years, both past and future. Café au lait served up along the inside of her wrist. She's fixing a martini for her old lady. Broken-down beer boxes lean against the sliding door behind their mother, eyes hooded in the kitchen's slate light. Peter's in the family room, keying bumps from his cling-wrapped eight of yay.

There's his father, appearing at the foot of the stairs. His parka's swollen at the paunch, his face at the cheeks, the night with gaining dark. "Kaleigh," he grumbles.

Without looking to their mother, Kaleigh abandons the half-made drink, brine dancing helicoid—DNA drifting in booze—and shuffles to the door. Her bag waits among her father's things near the front door.

"Saw it in your email last week, George," she spits, referring to their Amtrak tickets. "Fuck you think I'm not surprised right now?"

Ushering Kaleigh out the door, their father looks back to Peter one last time. Cold air rushes in to replace them.

There's Peter, later that night. He finds his mother in her usual spot on the couch, fifth of Svedka sweating on the coffee table. He wants to know where they've gone to.

"Off with that whore of his," she slurs. "Don't worry, yer sister'll be back."

Swollen nights, when she'd cornered him and whipped his cheek until his head walloped the wall. "You wanna eat don't you? There's yer dinner yer hidin you little shit." But now he's the one shaking her, the fear of no god in her eyes, just vacant terror, as if witnessing oblivion itself. He shoves her into the couch, swipes the Svedka, his keys off the rack, and wakes up in a ditch not too far from his house. He doesn't recall the drunk tank.

There's Peter, picked up by his buddy Robert Kaufman. He has nothing to his name but the shirt on his shoulders, his black chinos, and court papers. He's that hungover sort of hangdog, watching his own feet crunch over slabs of refried snow and slosh and mud. Mr. Kaufman's arm wraps his wife's shoulders on the doorstep.

Peter's welcomed into their big box of blueblood brick, but it's useful space, the house's is, allowing for communication from its farthest reaches. Behind the house spreads the bean-shaped pool surrounded by flagstone and flowers and beeches and pine. Like all the good in Peter's life, the Kaufmans' is more refuge than home.

He and Robert spend the weekend playing videogames in the basement, where a 65-inch TV chamfers the far corner. Not but a few years ago, Robert's dad lingered in isolation, properly varnished, lacquered, shellacked: Robert favors shiny euphemisms for his father's recovering alcoholism. The controller is passed between them but seldom a word, as if *shiva* is being held upstairs. Onscreen, Peter's avatar is brutalized by one of the several advanced war machines programmed to seek its demise.

"What is this, amateur hour at the Apollo?" Robert grimaces. "Gimme the sticks."

Dinner in silence. With Robert's brother off chasing his come-up in New York, Peter takes his seat, Robert and his father at either elbow. Chewing hot sausages and sweet peppers, Peter nods his fist, *Yes, the food is good.*

After three days, or maybe it's ten, Peter laughs. His laugh's impishly staccato like he's driving over mounds of dead mice and finding it much too funny. He starts talking again, too. About Dio and death metal and dirt bikes. About how he used a littered coffee cup to pick up Dodger's shit this morning. There's Peter, lurking behind a corner and scaring the pants off Robert. There's Peter ramming his fist into his friend's asshole and yelling *Jail simulation!*

There's Mrs. Kaufman, scolding Peter's empty diet of Red Bulls and processed carbs. There's Peter's rejoinder, "B-Vitamins," he enunciates, brandishing the can. Mrs. Kaufman squints and leans forward to better understand him, which seems to help despite its absurdity.

There's Robert setting the table. There's Mr. Kaufman, reading the evening news on his tablet. There's Peter, copying Robert's history homework. There's Mrs. Kaufman's default frown as she works an angry pot of beef stew and sizzling latkes, stomping for her husband, who asks if the boys will help. His tone assumes them deeply remiss to do such things, and he's right, they are, but they do them, and Mrs. Kaufman finishes cooking, and there's clapping and hollering and flailing. There's Robert, rapping his knuckles against the table and asking his mother, *Why doesn't Dad get shit for wearing a hat at dinner?*

Because he can't hear me when I tell him not to.

Mr. Kaufman plays innocent. Then, facing Peter, his finger traces crocodile tears.

There's Peter—*ptt*—fake spitting on the dishes he hands Robert to dry. There's their nightly TV session. There's Mr. Kaufman idling by, hands in pockets, perhaps missing the days when he was his son's favorite person, perhaps remembering what he's done to rattle his trust. There's his stunted English. It's robbed of articles and transition verbs. It says "fucky" instead of "fucking." It complains, "Man, the Dodgers sucks this year," meaning the baseball team, not their dog.

There's Peter, alone in the computer room as the unmistakable sound of Mr. Kaufman's gait breaches the French doors.

"Dodgers, what is he doing?"

Peter hears him fuss over their golden retriever before knocking and entering.

"Listen, Peter. If you need anything for school. *Money, books, whatever.* You take out loan, but we will *help*," he says, cursory signs supporting his words. "And look, if you ever want, we go to *meeting*, we be happy to have you."

Peter frowns and offers a stolid *thank you*, that backhand drawn from chin. His smile tight, Mr. Kaufman takes his leave, and Peter's head falls into his cargo fatigues. He isn't ashamed of Mr. Kaufman's offer, but that his gratitude is dressed in this black Gojira shirt.

There's Peter in the shower, leaning against bloom glass tiles, turquoise and teal and aqua marine. The water's gone cold but he doesn't notice. Mr. Kaufman's words reminded him he's going to college soon, clear across the country. And that he isn't their son.

There's Peter, getting high again. For whole nights he rides with Bryan Quackenbush, his skinhead connect who's basically Peter plus two years of coke abuse. They blow lines off a pocket mirror through rolled Washingtons. He endures Quackenbush's strength training diatribes— "And I say to him, You call that a fuckin set? You gotta go *parallel* bro. And this dude starts givin me lip about a knee injury and I'm like well you wouldn'ta gotten injured if you'da fuckin repped right the fuckin idiot"— because the coke's plentiful, especially during chiseling season. In the small hours Peter fumbles through the window he left unlocked, and sleeps through the day.

He plays suburban roulette, lucky every time he spins the chamber. He's dared to stand in the middle of Centennial Lane at the height of afternoon traffic. He tries for high fives from driversby. He pleads temporary insanity to Principal Macintosh—"I was in a fugue state from all the learning"—and is suspended three days. Not four days later he solicits a fight on the quad during gym. Their physical educator, Mr.

Sullivan, bores into the scrum and takes the brawlers into tender headlocks. To Peter's fortune, he doesn't report the incident.

There's Peter's GPA, flirting with the 2.0 minimum required by most collegiate admissions offices. Teacherly cautions flatter him with platitudes.

"You're too smart for this," said his math teacher, Mr. Thomas.

"Talent minus hard work equals destitution," said his chemistry teacher, Mrs. Stoltz.

"I taught your father here. He didn't have half the mind you do. You want to end up down Frederick Road, like him?" warned his English teacher, Ms. Neidig, who always encouraged Peter's love for bikes. "You want to wake up hungover just to pour cement? That kind of life might make for a good short story, but take it from me: suffering is a whole lot less worthwhile when you're the one undergoing it."

There's his scrunched baggie dotted with little green ribosomes, which Robert finds on the kitchen counter.

"Dude you can't just leave your bud out like that. They're Deaf, not blind," Robert says at the foot of the basement stairs.

Peter's still but for his thumbs working the joysticks. "My bad," he mutters.

The next morning Robert returns from the bathroom wrapped in a towel. "Forgot my—Dude, what the fuck?"

The towel seems to release Robert across the room. He grabs Peter's wrist and blows the powder off the wood stand. An elastic stillness, then Robert asks why he's doing this. Peter says he could ask the same thing, and is Robert going to compensate him for these losses.

"You mean Quackenbush though, right? Your sugar daddy?"

There's Peter shoving Robert where belly meets breastplate. There're Robert's small eyes glinting angry. There's a struggle. The lamp's knocked onto the bed. Peter uses Robert's collarbone to create distance before throwing the first punch. This ends the fight. Seconds later, Peter says he's sorry, but it's removed. He says it as if offering his friend an anagram, the meaning all scrambled. He says it in a way Robert can't refuse, without entendre, without hope for returning things to the way they were. Peter says it—"Sorry"—like glue applied to a broken toy.

There's Peter Fosch, a vacant form borne by his borrowed suit. He and Mr. Kaufman exit the Howard County Courthouse with expected results: license revoked for a year; 120 hours of community service; and a year of drug and alcohol counseling, followed by another three years with a general social worker. Without a word they get into the car and head back to the box of brick. Along the old Clark farm, where he'd gone paintballing with his pop, wheat grass and cattails and corn stalks bending in the wind. The trees along Breconshire menace them, their boughs snarling, boles shuddering, buds swaying like a newborn collective intelligence. Turreted stormclouds darken the sky. Drops drum up some business, bargaining by a thousand liquid bullets. Mr. Kaufman touches his hearing aid and glances at Peter as if to affirm the downpour through secondary sources of sound.

Trust in thine own eyes, Peter thinks, and nearly chuckles at the absurdity of it. He reaches for the envelope, Mr. Kaufman rapt at these exalted moments – hoping them exultant.

There's Peter Fosch, ripping open a letter, handed him prior to leaving for court that morning and propped atop their takeout coffees like a makeshift table. There's the University of Washington's crest above its masthead, the notary seal down near the dean of admissions' signature. Sandwiched between, the letter begins...

We're happy to inform you...

Meher Manda
poetry

Things I Do Extraordinarily: For the Immigration Overlords Who Demand a Proof of Excellence

1. Drinking my wrong coffee order in silence.

2. Spending an inexplicable amount of time dreaming up "what would my life be" routines. Like "what would my life be" if I was a singer with prodigious talent who smokes cigarettes purposely out of irreverence toward this said talent. "What would my life be" if I could be one of those girls who share healthy, transparent relationships with their mothers. "What would my life be" if I could be someone who loved and allowed herself to be loved?

3. Having an anxiety attack without troubling any one in my life. You would die in shock if you found out how sick I was.

4. Finding order in chaos. Cc'ing, my mind, my body, my notebooks, my writing desk, my bedroom, my relationships.

5. Avoiding death. Never once touching upon it.

6. Tearing up at little children performing badly on talent shows. For all those who know how awful they are, but who encourage them nonetheless. Where is this consideration for adults?

7. Finding new, never-before-considered ways to ruin whatever's left of my sad excuse for a relationship with my parents.

8. Saying I'm sorry ad nauseum. I could say it in sleep. Run me over with your lawnmower so I can apologise to you.

9. Having gut feelings, and never trusting said gut feelings, at repenting for having never trusted the gut feelings, at promising to hold that regret for life.

10. Convincing myself that America can be home, can be home, can be home, if I just close my eyes and try really hard. Is that not enough? Shall I go on? When can I stop? When does this stop?

First appeared in *Glass Poetry*

Turf

Mumbai, circa 21st century

The ladies compartment of the local train at rush hour is a battleground. The trains don't even have to stop for us to jump into the open door carriages because we are that skilled an army. The women at the front are the cavalry and if we don't charge fast enough we run the risk of toppling our reserves. That is how we look out for each other. We offer pregnant women seats. Touch their gravid bellies like seers looking for any sign of life in crystal balls. The train hauls over loudly but not loud enough to drown our singing. Of course we sing on our way to a fight. That is another way we look out for each other. By keeping spirits up. Sharing morning stories of incapable husbands and children born to become cogs in the wheels of the trains that keep us battling. We've never known the waters, the breeze that comes off of them, the very red of wine that is best had smelling the sea salt. We blush by lusting over strange men on billboards. We exchange photos and videos and dreams in the safe of the engine siren like contraband. Before we were here in these carriages, before these trains and tracks were here, this city was one big forest by the sea. This is why we lose ourselves in the woods of sharing. Why we nourish ourselves with five-rupee knickknacks from the hawker in the train. Buy scrunchies, earrings, garish, loopy chokers, only to toss them into the pits of our carry bags. So we can discover them after many days of nonstop war and remember the faint touch of nomadic friendships. *Amma* says that there comes a time every woman loses her will for combat. We too step out of our bodies, watch ourselves elbow, push, and jostle each other for space. Bicker over who stepped on whom, and who dragged whom, and much like all soldiers, beaten and haggard, we start to fall by first taking each other down. We become friends in treachery and for a short moment are this close to giving each other up when someone says something casual, a wisecrack or a particularly operatic movie dialogue to ease the tension and we fall for it and each other hard. I ask myself if the bodies of women are made to bear such beating but then someone reminds me that the state has always found a way to push down on all of us. And women have only just learnt to be considered a battalion, a squad, a troop, or whatever it is they are calling themselves for the revolution of the day.

Tequila Shot

Trivia

1. In the Velvet Underground song "I'm Waiting for the Man," Lou Reed goes to *this* avenue in Manhattan to score drugs.

Love

2. The Romeo of *this* real-life punk-rock couple claimed, "I never stabbed her; I loved her, but she treated me like shit," after his Juliet died of a stab wound to the abdomen. He then overdosed on heroin less than four months later. Who are they?

Animal Kingdom

3. *This* amazing species can survive air deprivation, radiation, dehydration, starvation, exposure to extreme temperatures, and even outer space!

Asia

4. Presidential elections in *this* country happen every five years, but there's only one candidate on the ballot.

Ancient History

5. Although his birth name was Gaius Caesar, *this* tyrannical emperor of ancient Rome is still known by his nickname, which means "little boots." He was also known for throwing wild orgies and committing incest with his sisters…in public.

Sean Dunne
poetry/nonfiction

My Past and Future in Present Tense

The verbal cipher
Excites gods to get hyper
The perfect perpetuity
Invites nods from lifers
But, way back in the day
Before I was an O.G.
When Ectoplasmic Cooler was my favorite Hi-C
I was lost
On the back of the bus
Beating on the seat
Talking to myself
Catching wreck on the street
Looking for trouble
Huddled up behind my house
In a bush
Up for three days
I couldn't stop it for my life
So, I pushed
Onto the next stop
And the next place
Where I could lose myself
I didn't realize
I would completely destroy
Mental health
Behind blue eyes
Exists persistence
I once knew
But it's lost
I'd catch a fade

Without hesitance
If it would pay the cost
For all the shit I did and didn't do
And things left unsaid
I wish I may
I wish I might
Wish I knew where to begin...

The open mic is held out of doors on the café's patio. Behind me, steady bouncing headlights and noises from traffic on Newport Boulevard reflect on the glass storefronts in the strip mall surrounding the café. They add to the perfection of the moment, giving it an urban aesthetic that is laced with the rosebud of my nostalgia.

And there she is.

Same as ever. Not the weary face that I behold from secret vistas in my current exile as she rushes our child off to school in the mornings. But the worry-free face of the young girl I met at the open mic, once upon a time.

Even though I've been up for three days on speed it couldn't be more perfect. I'm at that pleasant, dream-like, euphoric stage of insomnia and malnourishment, chewing on my tongue and fiend smoking Camel filters quite merrily. You see, speed addiction is a degenerative process. And this was before the degeneration. Before the voices. Before the psychotic episodes, the 51/50s, and prison. Before the guilt and shame that would eventually make it impossible for me to enjoy the high and yet paradoxically unable to stop. It is a commonplace affliction.

The second verse
I learned first
How to curse from the worst
I seen too much to write a rap without
Any bad words
Sometimes in life
The only way to say what you feel
Is just to use profanity

So,

Fuck it

Let's keep it real.

She was my one true love

I never thought she'd be mine

I used to just sit back and watch her

For a very long time

It was an "outside jam"

On a Wednesday night

At the local coffee house

She hosted the open mic

Her name was Courtney

And she played a lotta songs

From the Smiths

She looked at me sometimes

When she said certain lines

Just like this:

"If there's something you'd like to try...

If there's something you'd like to try...

Ask me,

I won't say no.

How could I?"

It took me something like six months

To finally get up the nerve

And even then

I had to do it through a poem

I transferred

My heart into a poem

And simply called it "For her"

I stood up at the open mic

And everything was a blur

Except for her

I saw her watching me

Through clouds in my vision

As if her life
Depended on the words I said
And
She listened raptly
I knew she knew that the poem was
For her
And just in case
I was mistaken
I paused to look at her
As I said the last line of
The poem
Her recognition told me that
I was no longer alone
So,
Please forgive my reminiscence
It's pertinent
In this instance
Talkin' about
Risin' above the pain
And going the distance
Necessitated
By life's terms
And I'll continue this narration
After these chosen words...

I sit there week after week, every Wednesday night, sleepless or not, spracked out or sober I show up. It is the longest I've ever held a job.

At home my world is falling apart. My father lost his job of many years and we are losing our apartment. When he isn't out looking for work, the old man sits numbly on the chair in his room, staring at the wall.

I do nothing to assist him monetarily.

To the contrary I take flight into the association of my druggie friends, staying up all night, smoking speed, staying as far away as I possibly can from the ruin at home, which is unfurling by many fathoms of tragic images with the sun that cusses each desperate day. Into the night I stow away all my treasures. Behind tightly drawn curtains in a tweeker pad filled up with teenage dope fiends, I fill up pages of journals with poetic prose, running scared from the obvious destruction that tears apart the stitches from the textile of my fading world. All with one monomaniacal purpose: to win the girl.

Biding my time in the vices of petty larceny and not so petty residential burglaries, Thursday through Tuesday, week after week, with that one single motive. And now here I am, peaking in my Courtney trip, exulting in the kaleidoscope of a dream deferred, all sorts of pleasure transmitting antennas going berserk in my brain. I find myself in front of the microphone. Courtney is sitting at the table closest to me. Everything else is a blur. Just she and I now as then forever the sum of a quantum physics equation. Just a matter of adding and subtracting and dividing and multiplying and remembering to Please Excuse My Dear Aunt Sally in the correct order of operations with the right combinations of numbers and there she will always be, staring at me from her little table with the coral green eyes.

The third verse
Is instrumental
In illustrating my thoughts
About the way that shit went down
And how I still pay the cost
For my transgressions
Her impression
Burns inside my soul
Cause now she's gone for good
And I'm alone
A half of a whole
I was a dope fiend
And I left a debt
That I never paid
I never was a proper father

To the child we made
It bothers me to this day
My world is shaded in grey
I can't appropriate
The proper words
That I need to say
But it don't matter anyway
Cause talk is cheaper than wishes
Conditional impositions
Turn us into willing victims
Perpetuating ultimatums
Demonstrating the sickness
That lives inside of us
By holding on to guilt from the past
Contingent on our willingness
Of which we know
To be vast
And it's a paradox
But so are many problems we face
The thing to do
Is focus on a way out
Of the disgrace
And move on

Cause she's gone...

But I'm still walking the line
Between obsession with the past
And how the future defines me

And now I'm on the county jail bus after sixteen hours in a holding cell, at court. The nighttime landscape of freeway-side flower mosaic perversities stream by in a familiar blur. I have to stand up on top of my

Juliet Fletcher
fiction

The Boyfriend Shirt

I want to wear it without drowning in it.

Right after Jack's departure, I found the boxy shirt he left behind. Time to take the scissors to it.

Out of the laundry bag where he'd bundled it, a ball of blue and grime, I pull it out and lay it down.

A T-shirt. XL not L, as he was before the sickness stole his weight. Before climbing the apartment's basement stairs brought him wheezing to the top, bent double on the Wayne Avenue sidewalk. He wore this second skin under his overalls.

With the shape stretched out, I hardly know what I am doing. I imagined a great shredding. A snip-snip revenge on memory with a pair of blades.

But a minute later, I think again. I look at the state of the shirt, dab the inky streaks, smell the dried damp.

This had been the one. Closing my insomniac lids, I see it on him, wet and heavy to lift off. Running coal-black streams down his long body. Ballooning with shower water that shot hot and steamy from a pitiful spout. Then hanging. Casting its shadow across the bathroom, the place he chose for long, silenced time-outs, his or mine. Heaped at last on the floor of the bathtub, sludge rinsing out, the shirt's dense heft clogging the drain-daisy.

He hadn't taken care of this skin, only shed it.

After loss, every consolation is small. Vindications can be smaller, droplets on a bathroom floor. Small comforts must be enough for me, as I know I'll keep the boyfriend shirt.

In the shops, women can pick up anything borrowed-boyfriend. We can buy boyfriend-cut jeans, boyfriend-cut socks. Sold as if lent.

A boyfriend shirt means a man's T-shirt for a woman. Straight-cut, untailored to any curve. Distressed, as if worn and torn from men's work.

Washed soft, and steeped in the traces of this dreamt-up lender, the one who'd give you the shirt off his back.

I used to laugh at what they hawked us, a store-bought proxy for caring. But here I am, reaching for my own.

Lips dry, I rock forward to a kneeling crouch, scissors in my untamed hand.

My boyfriend's shirt isn't yet a boyfriend shirt. Rough when pulled through my palms. A ring-neck built to withstand a thousand tugs.

The folds are sticky, full of work-dirt that never came out. From the day they sent Jack down a manhole, a smooth descent until the harness-reel jammed.

Slime, iridescent and black, soaked him through. Medics sliced away his overalls, but not the second skin.

"Is this the only work that matters?" My phrase, my fury. He threw that back at me for months.

"Not a stuffed suit," he'd said. He'd sipped scotch-soda for the sugar, and tracked the shoes walking past the top of our basement windows.

In our own corners, women spell out ways to save old castoffs.

"Rescue! Customize! Revive!"

I'm listening to Stacy-Super, whose screen tutorial is curt.

Her brows arch like a French insult, and I'd spring for the pinstripe nail-art on her polite talons. But her trill sounds keen to salvage this item, not aim spite.

"Fall back in love with an old one!" She's modeling a new T-shirt, on which she'll show her work. Each cut brave, each a transformation.

I start with the ring-neck.

I cut a line from the throat hollow out to the shoulder seam, rightwards, removing the front fabric. Same on the left side, to leave a balanced boat shape. This I mirror around back.

At first, I am cautious. Too far a cut, and the gape will widen, sliding and sliding the shirt off one shoulder until I lose patience.

But I flay a little more. When my boat sits like Stacy's boat, I pull the garment on.

"Feel that freedom to move." She's right, of course. I notice my own neck, my stance, a strong collarbone as I turn. I'm sad now that Jack ever had to struggle his shirt off. This boat would have saved him energy.

Next, I hold the sleeves. Stacy tells me I have choices to make.

When Jack's arms thinned out, his sickness joined us for every meal. Tendons pulleyed each time he reached for his fork. Not that he would let me interfere. Off to the bathroom he would go, to run the shower. Sometimes I could hear him washing. Sometimes I heard him talking to that lawyer.

They'd pursued a settlement, but these cases drag. When they'd met in arbitration, when they'd disputed contamination, I'd come too, carrying the files from his doctor's visits. Too heavy for him to hold with ease.

He'd clutched the small laundry bag, containing the only piece of physical evidence.

We'd hugged when we walked out of there, the tab for his treatment now billed to his boss.

But money for doctors became money for carers. His bearhugs lost their squeeze.

I opt to trim the sleeves, almost lose the arms.

But I hold back. I close the shear in a curve, so a little of the shoulder remains. Cap sleeves, which don't cover much in the end.

Pulled on once more, XL hangs like a ghost's sheet. Whether slashed or tied in knots, these lengths can go.

Jack had kept thinning, past L to size M. His weight has ticked up a pound or two, Nurse said, last time I stopped in.

Dust from the shirt silts off on my tile. I have invited exposure. Solvents, feces, scum. Toxins or cultures may thrive in the threads, even now.

Stacy has cut her back-pane with double diagonal slants. The shirt's herringbones hang now, a ribcage for her ribcage.

But this second skin of mine must not look skeletal. And knots, fringes, decorations take time I won't waste.

I nick the shirt's edges, breaking their hem-stitch. Then I tear across, letting the fabric find its way. When I'm done, the shirt ends in a jagged line, as unfinished as we are.

I pull it off my back. Where ash-gray silt streaks my skin, I rub it deeper, hitting every curve.

At night, I sleep naked, but if I wake at dawn with a yell, I fight to the surface.

I watch the sidewalk light ripple down from the street. I remember what was true in us, imperfect as hemmed pants and a homemade gown, a hand-darned partnership.

Then I'll pull the shirt down the sheen of my back, to wave my arms through the slits in this reclaimed fabric. It's all the proof I need.

Christopher X. Shade
poetry

In the Cancer Ward

Alone in their rooms
these twelve
the patients
put a knitted hat
on their oxygen tank
and band-aids for eyes and lips,
and name the tank Roger,
Gomez, or Edith.

They twirl their
intravenous tubing
coyly when
flirting with
nurses,
who astonish them,
who love them
enough to linger.

These twelve
the patients
whistle like whales
to other patients
and pass notes
by way of
nurses Malinowski
and Anna the Greek-Aussie,
these notes
are love letters
to themselves, like,

I wuv woo, and,
I must say
the blue brings out your eyes.

These ten then, these nine,
lying under sheets
for as long as they have
at this end of their lives
they've learned
to point and flex their feet
wiggle their toes
even baby toes—
they've learned,
lying in a bed,
how to jump for joy.

They schedule treatments
by the stars
in the night sky
out the window
and by animal care
calendars of cats
tacked above
them. This month's
orange tabby is
on her back too,
batting at a tinsel ball.
Her name, it reads,
is Rudy
and *you can take her home.*

These nine, these eight,
reach for the pen
and cross out yesterday

with a line.
Some days they draw
a lightning bolt,
other days a wave,
or a sine curve, either convex
or concave,
the geometries
of their bliss.

Ambulance Rides

The ambulance idles at the curb
all lights off,
up from Roosevelt Avenue
between blocks of buildings
these two paramedics
in the front seats
drink coffee from paper cups
they pour from a thermos
and try on each other's sunglasses
knuckle-roll coins
and fold intravenous tubing
into imaginary pets.

These two, on a recent night shift,
pulled a college kid out from under
an F train—
she'd been seen
for hours in Washington Square
tossing bowling pins up into the air
trying to learn to catch them—
she'd dropped herself
in front of the F
at 14th Street.

A day shift, today,
these two turn up the radio and sing
jazz splashing onto the sidewalk
while they can, between calls,
between summons to aid
the men in cardiac arrest
and the seizing teenage girls,
and last week the woman

who'd stood at a window for days
staring at the wall.
She was parched, soiled,
translucent—
and she fell into their arms, lost,
dead.

These days.
These two laze in their seats
play *I spy or somebody'll die*
or they don't
while they wait for what's next
while the wind outside the truck
whips up cigar wrappers
and lottery slips.

These two,
one of them sleeps,
face on the window,
and snores gentle coughs
while the other pulls watercolors
out from under her seat
and paints round full
wet circles of faces.

First appeared in *The American Journal of Poetry, Vol. 6*

Rachel Evans
nonfiction

Driving with my Father

I am nine years old. I have grabbed my patent leather purse, slipped into my ballet flats, and am tiptoeing out of the naughty man's house, following my mother and brother into the car. I sit in the back, my Laura Ashley dress bunching up beneath my sun-kissed legs. I turn around and stare at the house we just left. My mom drives quickly, leaving the dust to do its thing, leaving my father to discover his missing family, his missing car, his missing everything as he drinks with his friend on the rocking chairs in the backyard. I know a few things at this point: I know he drank too much for my mom to let him drive us home from Connecticut. I know he is not going to like that we abandoned him. I am both relieved and scared, relieved that I don't have to sit in a car with him as he swerves and weaves his way through other cars and the road. I am scared he will be so angry that he will come home and wreak havoc on our house instead of the road.

My father drives to be a man. There is something about the control he can exert onto a highway, the way he doesn't allow other cars or rules to tell him what he can or can't do. When he doesn't like what another driver does, the window is rolled down and his rage is spewed into the cold night. I have often been in the passenger seat, witness to this. "Dad, it's cold," I hiss through gritted teeth as I lower myself in the seat.

Here, now you have a better view of him. This is my present to you as you make me cold and uncomfortable. I love you that much.

I want to whisper these words to him, but I just sink further into the seat and repeat, "Dad..." I'm asking a question when I say it. "Dad?" I'm asking if he really needs to do this. No response. Two minutes ago, I was warm and enclosed; now it feels like everything is exposed.

"Hey! You motherfucker! Fuck you!"

Each "fuck" shoots past me, piercing the car next to us. I don't even know what specifically happened except that some sin has been committed by this stranger and it's my dad's responsibility to set him straight. I can only hope that the driver doesn't hear, that his windows stay closed, his ears shut to my father's madness.

When I am in middle school, he drives me to school in the truck he uses for his vending machine business. He holds the wheel in one hand and his coffee mug in the other, the coffee spilling on the dashboard or the area between our seats every time he stops short, which is a lot. Sometimes some of it splatters onto my shirt or jacket. When he slams on the brakes, a reflexive arm reaches out to protect me. I appreciate that arm, even if at twelve I intrinsically understand its futility. I arrive at school, kiss him goodbye, and am thankful to be in the care of other adults, anchored in one place. Opening a car door after a ride with my father is like taking a large and savory gulp of air after being underwater for way too long. I slam the door and exhale.

We are in a Denny's in Florida visiting someone's aunt. I am eleven or twelve; the years bleed together in my memory. At the payphone stands my father, attempting to make a call. The quarters are readily accepted but the phone won't comply. It is saying *No* to my dad, and he won't take *No* for an answer. So out comes the anger and fists and the Denny's pay phone doesn't know what hit it. It's not really a fair fight from the start, as my dad has more years on the phone and the injustice he feels at this broken machine towers over anything the phone might be feeling. Right now, all it's feeling is my dad's fists coming down hard, using its own handle as a weapon against it. My dad lands a hook to the right, but the phone's still standing; there's no knockdown eight count here. My father has anger and righteousness on his side but this phone is not going down easy; its numbers are staying intact, its cord still connected. Without a referee, my father continues to go punch for punch and the only audience is me, my mother, and my brother, cowering in our booth.

The Denny's staff is starting to notice so Mom nudges us, whispering, "Let's go outside to the car." She quickly pays the bill and the three of us wait anxiously in the car for my dad to finish off the phone, one last jab to the front, before he runs out to join us. He starts the car and slams on the gas and we escape from Denny's, our rented getaway car zooming down a Florida highway. I turn around to see if there are cops chasing us, if they've caught up with us, if we are all going to be arrested for the payphone brawl. Eventually we blend in with the seventy-five-year old retirees in traffic, and we are now incognito, just a normal family of four driving in the sweltering and depressing Florida heat. We drive on in silence.

All I can see of my mom in the front seat are her vibrant curls sagging with perspiration and I wonder if she's sleeping, if she's as sad as I am, or if she is numb. We are four fugitives. My brother, mother, and I, accomplices by way of blood and proximity. We all have anger problems and will be punished for leaving the scene of the crime. We just don't know when.

I am sitting in Wren Hall, the dorm I have called home for the last year. Sophomore year of college is finally over. I am moving out of my basement room and couldn't be more relieved. I won't have to live with Jess anymore, my angry, depressive, rave-going roommate. I won't have to share a suite with these girls, girls who do lots of drugs and talk behind each other's back, girls with whom I feel unsafe, girls around whom I can't be myself. Next year I will live in the Arts House, a place full of weirdos and eccentrics, people more like me, who value creativity and quirkiness over fraternities and pot. It has been a really hard year, one in which I found myself inexplicably sad and lonely but not fully understanding the origins of these dark feelings. I have been seeing a therapist and am starting to mine my childhood and the effect my dad's temper has had on me. Resentment toward my mom for not protecting me from him has been welling up in me and emerging in our sessions too. I think my therapist is subconsciously trying to make me hate my parents. And I'm worried it's starting to work.

I feel exhausted from finals and from being depressed and unhappy, but I'm still excited to go home and see my family and high school friends. I am not looking forward to the fact that home is not the same place I left before I started the year. My parents have moved to a small apartment for the summer. But I am leaving Wren Hall, and even if this new home is small and foreign to me, my family is there, so that makes it home. My stuff is all packed and I'm ready to go. I am waiting for my dad, who is picking me up.

"Guys, you have to come see this!"

As I'm sitting in my suite common room, someone I've never met comes running down and alerts my suitemates and me to the commotion in the parking lot. The rest of this memory is murky, but I am pretty sure the twisted feeling in my gut that told me my dad was part of this is real. I run outside and quickly learn what happened. My dad was honking his horn, angry that someone was blocking the front of the dorm. The person in front of him, a college student one year older than me, wasn't moving so my dad got out of the car and walked up to the driver's side, yelling for him to move. I can imagine the low timbre of his voice revving up as he steps out of his own car. I can see his hand opening wide and clenching. I can hear his loud voice bellowing as he walks up to the kid's window: "Move your fucking car! You're blocking every other person who would like to pass you and get where we're going!" I don't know if the kid yelled back or if he just sat there. He probably responded in some way; I would have. So my dad, on instinct, on impulse, on chemicals and wires crisscrossing in his brain, reaches out his arms and puts his hands on the guy's neck. He grabs him because he's angry, because this little twenty-one-year old has more leverage than he does, because he blocked him from getting to his daughter.

The kid is fine. But he is understandably shaken, and he is talking charges, lawsuit, something. And worst of all, he is friends with the girls from my suite, the ones I am so happy to be escaping. Somehow I convince him not to file charges.

"Your dad has real problems! He's fucking crazy!" he yells at me as we walk away. I want to hit him, call him names. It's completely irrational after what my father has done, but I still want to stand up for him. I don't want to defend what he did, but I want to tell this prick that he can't talk about my dad like that, because he's my dad and only I can be mad and hurt about what he did. Instead I nod. Because I also can't disagree with him. But right now, I'm stuck. I want to leave this awful year and dorm situation and my only getaway car is with the bad guy. The tears are falling fast and I am angry and numb at the same time. It's disorienting and confusing to feel so full of one emotion but also so empty from another.

We pack up the car, and drive back to New York. I won't talk to him. He is behind the wheel and there is no air in the car and my stomach is being washed out, empty of all the hope I felt a few hours earlier. It's a five-hour drive from Boston so I will myself to close my eyes and fall asleep. I don't want to look at my dad, or the image of that boy in my head, his face red with anger, his finger pointing at my father and me, accusing us of being bad. I don't want to look out the window and see the world as we drive by; I am angry at it for witnessing the secret of my dad's temper every time he unveils it. When we pull into a strange block and he parks in the driveway, apologizing again, I realize I have no home anymore.

"Hey dad, do you want to go in and break the pay phone?"

Over the years, my brother and I would tease my father with this question whenever we drove by a Denny's. It is a testament to my family's resilience and sense of humor that years later we could laugh about that long-ago brawl. I realize now that our choices were either laughing or crying, to scrunch up our faces into a smile or frown, dropping into our bodies as we remembered. We couldn't ignore any Denny's we passed, but we could choose how to remember. We opted for the former.

Everyone in my family was shaped and molded in different ways by these incidents and others. My mother fought my father, yelling back or standing between his shouts and us. She protected him and she protected her children. She was strong and weak in the same moments. When she drives, she speeds and stops suddenly whenever there is a car or obstacle in front of her. It makes me queasy to sit in the passenger seat, moving so quickly only to stop short a moment later, my stomach lurching with the car. She holds on so tightly to the wheel that she developed a medical condition, dupuytren's contracture, where bubbles of tension built up in her hands, affecting the way her fingers curved, which required hand surgery. I find that she too weaves into other lanes sometimes, steering clear of the dangers that lurk at the edges of the highway. It's as if she's still racing away from that big house in Connecticut, shouldering her children from harm, yet braking for my father, the push and pull of love controlling and tightening her own hands on the wheel.

It's impossible to be in a car with my family and not be reminded of the ways in which we grew from our history and into ourselves, the people we become when we drive on an open road. The irony is that now my father rarely raises his voice while his children struggle with the ways his voice has shaped them. With the help of medicine, aging, and a softening of his unhealthy heart, the rage-filled man has transformed into someone else. He is soft and apologetic about that other person, the one he never had to be afraid of because he was inhabiting him. He doesn't remember these moments embedded in our memories as well as we do. It's as if he was there but as someone else, that other person no one recognized. But my brother and I still remember.

My brother dances in and out of lanes, speeding past his surroundings. The blue veins in his long neck begin to shine brighter, and his face reddens as he takes control of the road. The horn provides a steady soundtrack, mixing with the cacophony of his frustration with other drivers and my fast beating heart. He does not always drive like this, but when he does, I am reminded that we are the products of our parents' wiring, sparking up and down the dial of madness, depression, joy, humor, and love.

And me, well I am happiest in a car when I am driving alone. I hold the power in my hands, in my legs, in all of me to speed up, to brake, to take my life, my every moment, in whatever direction I choose. That freedom feels best when the windows are rolled way down, the radio is playing a song that moves me, and my mind is a paintbrush working the canvas of the road as I move along it. I let go of the past, of expectations for the future, and I take the road as it comes.

Shirley Temple

Trivia

Mythological Creatures

1. According to medieval lore, only *this* type of person can tame a unicorn.

Games

2. Though now exclusively played by children, fully armored Roman soldiers once played *this* game to improve their footwork, and the original courts were over 100 feet long.

Banned Books

3. In *this* author's frequently banned novels, young characters masturbate, menstruate, and have wet dreams, among other universal experiences of puberty.

Name that Movie

4. In *this* film, a bookworm talks to silverware and furniture while trying to civilize her barbaric captor.

Childhood

5. A stencil, a puzzle lock, a spinning top, and a character-shaped eraser were the first toys to come with one of *these*.

Emily Brout

fiction

Sunshine Boy

One morning, I was a child. I got out of bed, hurrah for me, to find my dad standing at the kitchen sink staring out into our backyard with a cinematic yearning. He had been depressed in bed for weeks, but now he was out of bed standing at the kitchen sink watching a squirrel through the window, mesmerized.

"Glorious," he said.

I was not sure what was so special about it, other than its balls being too big for its body. Poor thing was rolling around trying to get his hands on some nuts, but every time it got close, the nut would get farther away. My father scooped some peanut butter out of a jar with a spoon, weighing down his tongue. His voice lowered and took on that distinct lathered in peanut butter sound where all letters turn to L's. L for loneliness, L for what wrong decisions I made to relate so viscerally to a squirrel whose balls are his own undoing.

"So beautiful," he said.

He just stood there staring. I never saw him look so light. At the time I just figured it was just some really special peanut butter.

Not long after I saw this, I was in the car with dad and my mother. We were on our way back from the doctor's office and we waited in the car as my dad ran into the toy store. When he came back out, he got into the car and gave me a toy squirrel. It was made out of felt and was full of so much plush that it was stiff.

When my mom asked why the squirrel he explained that no one thought much of them. In fact, a lot of people hated them because they reminded them of greedy little financiers with cocaine addictions, but secretly squirrels had special powers.

"Squirrels see the potential in every nut to become a tree," he said.

He explained that they are the most empathic and patient animals and that they believed in him. He knew they did because when he was close to them their sunshine came out and he could feel the warmth they had for him. To prove it, when he saw a family of squirrels he pulled over to the side of the road.

"See! Don't you see it?" he said jumping up and down. "The sunshine!"

We did not see anything, just some squirrels with some nuts twitching. We watched his hand hover over them. When he finally touched one, his eyes went so wide and his smile got so tight it made me think of snapping box springs.

"I can be a tree," he said.

It probably should have scared me.

It didn't matter if it was true or if it wasn't. For the first time, my father felt special. For the first time, he started talking at cocktail parties, and eating a lot of nuts. During the weekends he would spend hours in the backyard with the squirrels. He would stand next to a tree clenching his fists trying his best to photosynthesize. For a year, dad was happy.

Then one day, as I was doing homework in my bedroom, I heard the sound of him sobbing.

"What's wrong?" I asked.

"Their sunshine," he said. "It's gone."

He stopped looking out the window. He stopped trying to photosynthesize. Every morning during pancake hour he'd threaten my mom that if he didn't find a job soon he would drive to the city, find the sharpest skyscraper, and jump off of it. Every night he would mope around again with his jar of peanut butter looking outside the kitchen window waiting for the squirrels to believe in him again.

I knew I had to do something, so I invented a game. I called it "Talk My Stuffed Squirrel off the Skyscraper." I had dad put the stuffed squirrel at the edge of my bed, and I would tell it all the things it would miss if he jumped off.

"Motorcycles, scraping the dirt out of your fingernails, the sound of fizzy seltzer after you put a lime in."

"You," he said.

"Me," I said.

When we were done, he said, "One day you will be a tree. You don't need anyone else's sunshine."

As I got older, we stopped playing the game. When you are young and your dad is sad you get sad too and make up games, but when you are older and your dad gets sad you just get scared and you hide. Your sunshine slips away.

One night, when I was in high school, my dad came into my room eyes so puffy from crying they looked like stuffed shells. He had not brushed his teeth in weeks so his breath smelled like burnt tires.

"Can we play stuffed squirrel?" he asked, holding the old toy.

This time I was not scared. I was just tired.

"Please?" he asked.

"Can you just function?" I asked.

He didn't say anything. He just stared at me for a minute and left the bedroom. I could hear the sound of him revving the engine of his motorcycle. That night he rammed his motorcycle into a tree in search of warmer places.

If I were warm like the squirrel I never would have said that to him, but I am not warm. I am a cold person. A bad person. How do I get my sunshine back? Maybe I never really had it? I spend hours looking out of our kitchen window. If it worked for dad it could work for me, right? I wait for something magical, but nothing happens.

I know I have to do something to get my sunshine back. My dad could always find the sunshine hiding inside of things, but I've never been able to. Maybe I have to make the sunshine myself?

In the basement I tinker at it all night with my father's tools, his old motorcycle, and all of the electrical supplies I can find, the wire and conduit identifications, and when the sun came up I am done. I go upstairs excited to show my mother in the kitchen. I tell her to sit down, and with dirty oil stained hands, I roll my dad's old motorcycle up the stairs to show her my invention.

"It's a safety precaution for cars and motorcycles."

I put my hands on the new and improved steering wheels and pretended to rev the engine. "The steering wheel or handlebars analyze your sweat to detect the presence of cortisol and other stress-related neurochemicals that indicate when you probably shouldn't be driving."

I tell her it is a "Breathalyzer for Your Brain." I explain how when someone is too stressed or suicidal and shouldn't be driving, my invention can do four different things, depending on the setting. It can put on relaxing music, it can alert loved ones so they can call you and tell you why you shouldn't crash your motorcycle, or call a guy like me, not a son, but somecone like me who is able to talk a stuff squirrel down from the ledge of a bed.

That night, when mom's asleep, I stare out the kitchen window one last time. I see some squirrels. At first I see no sunshine, but then they catch my gaze. They notice me looking at them; the sunshine does not come out in beams as expected. The rays are subtler. They are trapped in their eyes.

Shawn Shafner
poetry

Love Poem 3

If these words could be kisses
I'd cover you in the dictionary
Wrap you tightly from Ahh to Mmm,
Lay bound with you till Zzz
My quill caressing down your spine.
I'd compare your thighs to summer days,
Take the road less traveled around your lips
To be or not—too beautiful.
With you my tongue learns new languages
A pop sugar
Four letter
Most graphic novel
Ellipsis quivering like lightning conducted through dots unconnected
Caught like the breath
Stuck in my chest
Because words are not kisses and never can be
And your ink is the coolest drink I've ever known.
I'm so awfully thirsty
And sick of the QWERTY
So just hold me.
Be near me.
Let's use our five senses—
Describe the world before words.

Ode to the Unicorn

When he was born
Unicorn had a horn
Erupting from out of his head.
But you know how it goes
A space there now grows
That invites something else instead.
For the unicorn found
A great love for the ground
And shed his fine feathered wings.
He galloped apace
Spinning fire and lace
To shelter the beds of the kings.
Why the unicorn lost his goatee, no one knows.
Some say it was plucked for the shroud that he sews
For the earth he loves dear—
The one you're on right here—
That same globe we inherited once.
It's been through revolution,
Upheaval, pollution,
The blood streams unstemmed from the hunts.
Now the unicorn's tears
Were bottled as beers—
Just one drink made violence seem gay.
Once his tail, now a whip
And his cloven hooves slip
'Neath the weight of the gold that we pay.
Men have driven the beast off the cliff in a rage,
Then they laugh, tell their friends, have a smoke, turn the page.
"His problem, not mine.
Unicorn shouldn't whine,
He should fix it or give up and die."
But the unicorn knows

Death makes love with what grows.
He doesn't give up but he sighs,
"The road is too long
I'm not young or so strong
As I once was, but that's how things pass.
I gave all that I had
Both the good and the bad
Now it's time to lie down in the grass."
So the unicorn's body became a deep well
And the people made pilgrimage to where he fell
And slaked their thirst with a story to tell
Of how heaven was born from the dark mouth of hell.

Noam Osband
lyrics

The Luna Moth Song

The luna moth looks lazy
But its life is rather crazy
Hatching flying, quickly dying
In just days

The moths are made without a mouth
No way to kiss or to go south
No time to wine or dine
Just time to go get laid

How intense moth romance must be
If each sunset that they do see
Is one $1/7^{th}$ of the sunsets they will know

One week to meet, one week to wed
One week beside their lover's head
One week to make all the sweet moth love they will know

Lord let me live just like a luna
Let my heart be straight and truer
Than those other animals
Wasting longer lives

I've no time to take for granted
The sweet pheromones you planted
I want to lay between your winged thighs

Baby we've no time for games
We've just one week, it's such a shame

No time to fly down, take that trip to El Salvador

Cause we've one Darwinian need
So lean back lover and take my seed
Cause mating is what luna lives are for
Mating is what luna lives are for

Joel Remland
nonfiction

Escape Artist

It felt like an hour, but couldn't have been more than fifteen minutes since the rapping at the door, and the ensuing panic. The young occupants alternately froze, scattered, yelped, started to pray. But the jig was up as Beitler swept through, herding the entire group from the hotel suite, where a cadre of typically respectable eighth grade boys had arranged an ill-fated rendezvous with their female counterparts. While nothing remotely improper had occurred, not a cheek kissed nor even a hand held, the mere suggestion of a closed door in mixed company was enough to send Beitler, nominally a rabbi, into a self-righteous rage. As they filed out, he berated the perpetrators with a verbal onslaught of fire and brimstone, declarations of disappointment, and promises of hell to pay.

Before turning to leave, he barked a parting warning to the now vacant room: "If anyone is still hiding in here, you're gonna be in even more trouble unless you come out right now!" The threat was sufficient to shake loose one last holdout from her hiding place, the girl blubbering as she pled with him not to call home. Offering no solace, Beitler ushered her out, glancing back once more before letting the door slam shut behind him.

Or so he wanted me to believe. I convinced myself of the likelihood that Beitler had executed the classic fake exit maneuver and now lay in wait, relishing the chance to bust the one who got away. Unfortunately for him, hide and seek was my game. So there I stood stock still behind the room's floor-to-ceiling curtain, intently studying the cross-hatch pattern of burnt orange canvas pressed to my nose. Focusing on the fabric helped calm the blood throbbing in my ears, and beat back my creeping pubescent paranoia, whispering all too assuredly that the tips of my shoes were showing out the bottom of the curtain.

Deprived of visual stimulus, my imagination swirled, conjuring a vision of Beitler's morbidly obese bulk propped on a corner of the sagging bed, his oversized felt yarmulka perpetually slipping from his receding hairline as he dabbed his sweaty brow with a snot-encrusted hankie. For an instant, the potential for this unfolding cat and mouse scenario struck a faint note of familiarity, before I made the connection. *Schindler's List* had just hit theaters, and was practically mandatory viewing for American Jews of all ages and denominations. That horrifying scene of the boy beneath the latrine still fresh in my mind, I nearly laughed out loud at the absurd irony of me, likely the only half-blooded Jew within twenty miles of this dilapidated Catskills hotel, hiding from an over-zealous, bumbling rabbi enforcer.

Not that Beitler made it all that difficult to evade capture, reluctant as he was to actually bother checking the obvious places. He relied instead on the fear of God, which worked well enough to make mensches of us, his students.

After fifteen minutes, or maybe an hour, I realized I couldn't hear his belabored breathing, and worked up the courage to hazard a peek, convinced all the while that the instant I chose to reveal myself would be a split second too soon, that Beitler had chosen the next moment to abandon the hunt. I took a deep breath and stepped hesitantly from behind the curtain to find the room empty.

Exhaling relief, I surveyed my surroundings, and was just starting to formulate an escape plan when I heard rustling behind me. My heart leapt and stomach sank as I turned to see a girl emerge from behind the other curtain framing the window, just feet away from where I had been ensconced.

Peri was petite, with a pale heart-shaped face and doughy eyes that presently wore a look of profound dread. We might have been better acquainted if the Orthodox Jewish school we attended hadn't been segregating us by gender since fifth grade, our classrooms relegated to different floors, just as our rooms were now at this school-sponsored religious weekend retreat.

After shaking off the initial shock of unexpected company, we exchanged a few frantically-whispered words and pantomimed gestures about what to do next. I was still ecstatic over my narrow escape, but Peri was starting to hyperventilate, tears welling at the corners of her eyes.

Hailing from a more observant family than mine, she had more to lose. My dad had died a few years prior, so I had no one waiting at home to reprimand me, least of all my widowed shiksa convert mother, who would think it entirely natural that thirteen-year-old boys would want to spend time in the company of girls. Peri's parents would not be so understanding.

Still, even if there would be no repercussions for me at home, getting caught alone with a girl in a hotel room would not be viewed charitably by Beitler and the school authorities, who would soon realize that we were missing. For both of our sakes, we had to make our move, and quick.

Surprising myself by taking charge, I motioned for Peri to stay where she was while I tip-toed over to the door's peephole. But I was too short, still awaiting my growth spurt, and had to silently drag the heavy wooden desk chair across the matted carpet over to the door and stand on it to get a better view. All clear.

The danger inherent in our escapade must have sparked some identification with TV and pop culture stereotypes, where the guy saves the girl in some grandiose gesture of romantic heroism. While I never thought of Peri in that way, the narrative seemed to fit our circumstance so well, I started to believe it my mission to spirit her to safety.

Knees shaking in her ankle-length denim skirt, I reassured Peri with the most convincing-sounding platitudes I could muster: "Don't worry, we're going to get you out of here," and "It will all be okay," realizing, even as the words left my mouth, the futility of promising anything. But I needed her to stay calm, at risk of giving away our location.

Lucky for Peri, my brief life experience up to that point had favorably predisposed me for success in just this sort of spy extraction exercise. For years I had been pretending to abide by the same Orthodox traditions as my classmates, all the while leading a secretly secular home life, replete with profane indulgences like flipping the light switch on and off on Saturdays.

Terrified that my school peers would uncover the truth and ostracize me for it, I honed my skills of deception and assimilation, learning to mimic the rhythmic motion of sincere prayer, feigning familiarity with their esoteric beliefs and practices.

The minutes passed, and Peri's hand-wringing only grew more frantic. I again checked the peephole, and this time saw Beitler's hefty frame barreling down the hallway. From thirty feet away, I could feel the floor rumble with each step as he hurtled towards us. Then rapid-fire banging on the door. We froze in place. A count of ten and Beitler's beefy paw rapped again, then aggressively jangled the door handle. I envisioned a split screen scene right out of a movie, he with his ear up to the door to discern any signs of movement, us holding our breath and bracing for impact. If I had a gun, I'd be pointing it up to the peephole, aiming squarely at his face.

In that hanging moment where seconds are minutes, Peri and I locked eyes, reading the fear in each other's. Anticipating the slide of a key and turn of the deadbolt, the pregnant silence instead gave way to a most unexpected sound: though dainty and muffled, Peri had audibly, unmistakably farted.

Exercising restraint and sparing Peri further embarrassment, I pretended not to hear a thing, even though it was the only thing to hear in that deadened, confined space.

Before I could even begin to process the implications of this encounter, another barrage of door banging and knob twisting ensued. We could sense the desperation in Beitler's movements, and while still holding our breath, he turned and waddled back down the hallway. Suspecting he would soon return to the scene of the crime with a key, I seized the moment to make our escape.

I steeled myself and opened the door, looking left then right to ensure the coast was clear of Beitler or any number of rabbi's wives who patrolled the hallways as chaperones. Then I hastily shepherded Peri to the nearest stairwell, which somewhat anti-climatically was just a few feet from the door. She thanked me with a look, and we parted ways without a word.

Trying to nonchalantly slip back into the crowd proved as difficult as assimilating into the school community in the first place. I milled about in the hotel lobby and other public spaces trying to join conversations already in progress, until one classmate called my bluff, alleging I was among those captured. I flatly denied it of course, insisting that if I were, how could it be that I was standing there talking to him?

Word had filtered down that after rounding up the offenders, Beitler kept them incommunicado while he called each of their parents in turn, demanding they drive three hours each way to collect from the hotel the walking disappointments that used to be their children. I was sure he had threatened those caught up in the sweep, pressing them to identify anyone who might have escaped, maybe even offering leniency if they named names. But the fallout from the scandal soon dissipated, and I walked free, apparently cleared of further suspicion.

Later that afternoon, I found myself chatting with a female friend who abruptly intimated that *someone* might have a crush on me. It didn't take much imagination to deduce that it was Peri. By early the next week we were chatting awkwardly on the phone, and following the trajectory of most middle-school relationships, our flirtation was over by week's end.

Two years later, during my freshman year that would prove to be my last in Orthodox Jewish high school, I would occasionally spot Peri in the hallways. She had blossomed into a pretty young woman, her confidence buoyed by her now ample bosom that attracted the attention of upperclassmen, at whom Beitler—still the overbearing shlemiel of a rabbinical studies teacher—would bark his reprimands.

We never spoke again, but the couple of times Peri returned my gaze, I could sense an unspoken bond, a tacit agreement to bury the memory of what passed between us in the hotel room. Because if Orthodox Jewish school taught me anything, it was how to be an escape artist. If it taught me anything else, it was how to be a mensch and keep a secret.

Whiskey Neat

Trivia

Magic

1. *This* magic word or incantation means "I create what I speak" in Hebrew and was often written in the shape of a triangle on an amulet, where it was believed to possess healing powers.

Escape from Reality

2. Aldous Huxley wrote *The Doors of Perception* after taking *this* drug to escape from selfhood and his ordinary mode of consciousness.

The Supernatural

3. In the Egyptian underworld, if your heart was lighter than *this* you could pass safely into the afterlife.

Dreams

4. Three days before his death, *this* historical figure supposedly dreamed of mourners surrounding a corpse, which turned out to be him.

Games

5. There are more possible positions in *this* game than there are atoms in the observable universe.

Amanda Miller
poetry

god talk

talking god with eleven-year-olds
we sink into centuries of concepts illuminated
by jewish clergy, philosophers, mystics, scripture
slides curated by a cohort of reconstructionist jews
who handpicked the most palatable perspectives for this power-point

a god slow to anger, abounding in kindness
a god who shapeshifts and can appear in human form
a god who creates and controls, but permits free will
a god who authors supernatural miracles
a god non-anthropomorphic, beyond human comprehension

no mention of that narcissistic, insecure God
that God who terrorizes and destroys
though if the kids have had half an eye open
they should be well aware of Him by now

the kids squint and giggle
doodle and shrug
peek at their phones
contort into pretzel shapes
sneaker laces dangling

what time is it?
6pm
can i use the bathroom?
you don't have to ask

god as mystical changing energy

god as a cosmic process
god as electricity
god as magnetism
god as love

a pause

have you ever studied astronomy, i say
have you ever considered the vastness of the universe?
doesn't it just blow your mind?

they nod, straighten up, cock their heads to one side
then it's three, two, one, blast off:

i'm talking cosmos and galaxies
scrolling through slides
reading this quote and that passage
presenting this image, that question
asking why do you think so many people have been thinking about this
for so many centuries in every culture across the globe?
thinking
ruminating
questioning
wondering
making up stories
scrawling down myths
trying to crack this nut, this mystery of existence
or at least produce a hairline fracture
i'm getting real passionate now
saying it's all just so crazy
isn't this all just so crazy?
infinite space?!
birth and death?
a time before we existed, a time we will no longer exist

isn't it completely unfathomable?
doesn't this just blow. your. mind?
this is why people can't stop talking about god.
this is why!

they're more alert now
eyes all the way open
one girl raises her hand and says
there's gotta be another planet in the universe like ours
with humans like us
who didn't make climate change
i say yes that could be true!
i don't know!
we don't know!

then we're out of time
have a good week i say, closing the laptop
they pack up and head home for dinner and homework
some say you too
others just disappear

i glance at the empty chairs
throw on my jacket
pick up my bag
open the door
into the fifty-five-degree breeze
it was ninety yesterday
i've got whiplash from the weather
it's twilight in brooklyn and i'm walking through the rain
the sky is slate gray with a hint of blue
like a mixture of smoke and water
or ash and water
like the ganges

—sacred—

i've written this word on the board several times
asked the kids if it's a word they recognize
yes, they've said, pronouncing it "scared"

the rain is coming down harder now
and the sky has transferred its light to my chest
an electric current runs through the front of me
i want to drop down on my knees
i want my forehead to kiss the concrete
i want to feel the raindrops against my back
like the tiny fingers of the child i may never have
to assure me that the creation of life is an act of divinity
mirroring the creation of a star

but i don't drop down
instead i stay still
leaning my body against a brick building
propped up by shadow
i can't stop the electricity
i want to run into the street, stop traffic
cars parting like the red sea
as i throw myself face down on the asphalt
knees tucked under my chest

child's pose

oh god,
author of supernatural miracles,
i want a miracle
i want the ground to swell and shake
crack and break
i want hot lava to shoot up through my fingers

and i want to see god's face
in a pillar of smoke and cloud

Melissa Shaw

nonfiction

The Rabbi's Pants

The Rabbi's sweatpants are blue and have elastic bands that gather and pucker, you know, around the feet and the waist. That kind.

They are also the kind that you have no choice but to wear a little too high.

They are an old man's pants.

The kind of pants that end up at Goodwill. They look like nothing at all.

The Rabbi is ninety-six.

I came to the Rabbi's apartment just as I had been doing. Mondays at two. For an hour or so.

That day I showed up in my ratty jeans.

The ones that all too often show off the very top of my butt crack—that little squeezed valley that might become obscene if the pants were down any farther.

I really don't know why they do it.

They are a size 12.

But, even with a belt, I always have to pull them up. I've always thought it had something to do with my hips.

The Rabbi didn't go to the Holocaust.

He was invited, of course, although he had to regretfully decline.

He was in America in the '40s. He missed that once in a lifetime shindig where his first wife was killed.

And his one and only daughter.

The Rabbi also wasn't at Woodstock. But many of his friends from the '60s were. The thinkers, the believers, the swamis, the chiefs—the people who still make God-music—wherever they are.

We had been meeting this way for a while.

Eating Chinese food, heating it up in his microwave, three minutes on high, and talking about Shekinah.

While I asked him a question about Torah that one Monday, the Rabbi secretly looked at my Levis (these ones that I put on every day, pretending that they are cleaner than they are.) I pretend that no one notices the street murk around my feet.

I pretended I did not notice his shifting glances.

But still—I know he knows I did.

Somewhere in a lull in conversation, somewhere around the destruction of the temple, he stood up, leaning on his cane.

The aging Kabbalist shuffled through his apartment on 96th Street.

With little more than a word, he went to his bedroom. He'd be right back, he said.

He returned holding his blue sweats behind his back. He asked me: please put these on.

He threw them to me for emphasis and I caught them.

"Right now?"

"Yes, right now. Why not? What else is there?"

He said the pants I was wearing no longer suited me.

Apparently, I had upgraded to an old faded pair of previously, Jewishly owned sweatpants. Men's size "M."

He reminded me to always recognize what I had outgrown and to be ready to let go.

The Rabbi had just gone through a divorce. He left his third wife, who he claimed was killing him. She was too old for him.

She was sixty-four.

He had always lived in America.

I do not think he ever went back to Hungary after the war. No, not even for a visit.

He walked back out of his living room to get some tea for us, so I could have privacy to change.

I slipped off my jeans. My buckle clanked as my dirty denim hit his floor. I was in my underwear at the Rabbi's.

I looked rather funny in the Rabbi's sweatpants. They fit, in a way, worse than my jeans. My thighs, too aware of each other with no structure, flapping in heavy cotton.

The Rabbi was never mad at life or God, even after he found himself widowed as a thirty-something. Even when his very beloved second wife died at forty. And no, not even now, a divorcee-starting over again after a third marriage.

He says the answer is joy. He says joy is the thing that takes the sadness out.

He says he wakes up screaming, "I'm alive!" at the sun. Every morning he says thank you to the heavens. He has been known to kiss the sky, his palms in prayer. The good inclination coming together with the bad—that is what he says prayer is.

I took off my pants at the Rabbi's behest. I had to. He was waiting in the kitchen picking at the Chinese leftovers waiting to get back into Numbers.

Sheila-Joon Azim
nonfiction

Peanut Butter and Jelly

Razorback Mountain was still pink with morning as our camp of fourteen left with no trace. Eric, Christian, Anthony, Tatiana, and Racheal were all in the back of the white SUV with Mac and me in front. We were a Sesame Street representation of diversity and inclusion, dust equally in every pore of our skin, bones aching and bruised with the labor we had just finished. My food anxiety had transformed into making sure others had eaten, completing the *Metamorphosis* theme of this year's Burning Man with my own radical healing. Campmates, true to New York form, would overexert themselves, forgetting to eat (with that slight look in their eye), not even blend cold-brew before working, and then wonder why they were so on edge. I took it upon myself to see to our well-being and was named the camp "fluffer" for offering water and snacks, suggesting breaks—and proudly fulfilled these duties. I had a plan to make us a variety of PB and J's once we were waiting in line for Exodus. I spent the day before defending my paper-bagged goods, tucked under the last of the fold-up tables as we scurried to pack our camp. The time for sandwiches had arrived and I foraged the car for something like a butter knife to execute the mashing of nuts and berries. Mac was in a mood, still. He discouraged the sandwich endeavor as unnecessary and impossible. Racheal handed me a light green Sharpie that I enthusiastically disinfected. I took the defended breads (which had been in the desert sun for the previous ten days) and on the back of a notebook, laid out the pieces on top of the SUV's once white, now dust-covered hood.

I returned to the car, finding heads slumped this way and that with more exhaustion, dreamy retrospections, and ruminations than one story could carry and said, "Order Up!" ignoring Mac and his jagged edges, razor dangerous with sunny pinks on his back too. One by one I delivered the sandwiches and what remained of the cold-brew mixed with almond milk. We ate together. Mac had one too. Sugar hit tired brains and blood circulated in our bodies. Conversation flowed: Burning Man, its 70,000 friends, the elephant art from Russia, the vignettes Christian and Tatiana had put on Youtube, Anthony's positive relationship with social media and how it can serve us, not us it. I expressed my deepening frustration at being the invisible minority in a time of radical inclusion in casting, disparaging shows like *High Maintenance* and *Orange is the New Black* for not giving me appointments because I didn't look Middle Eastern enough, or queer enough, or crazy enough, even though I am, enough. Eventually, even Mac came around and shared a poem he had been working on. We were screaming with hysterics and delight at the simple brilliance he had captured. Our car began moving, and we prepared to leave our desert home.

We arrived in Reno feeling satisfied, amplified, happy, our smiling faces lined with the desert's gracious, sometimes obliterating sun. Once we finished the grueling labor of unloading, our camp finally made it to the hotel, blinded by casino sounds, tobacco smoke, and the glares of locals. Others mocked the locals as sad, doing cartoonish impressions. But why not them? Their lives were as mysterious as anyone's, and surely they had as much human potential as we did—if we'd learned anything during our infinite desert week in an alternative society, wasn't it that? Human potential? Why not recognize them rather than buy into the instantaneous "othering" that we expected them to project onto us? Were we not then hypocrites?

Mac and I had decided to spend two nights to ourselves in Lake Tahoe, just an hour away. We drove to the magnificent lake, a world away from Reno. We missed our friends already, missed splashing around in our beautiful new bodies of perfect shapes and curves and complexions, ordering Mai Tai's and Cucumber Coolers. But we were greeted in Lake Tahoe with kindness and met other Burners from New Zealand at a hut bar on the beach, recognizing the dusty cars that passed us and offering friendly waves.

I noticed a shift in culture—there was more money here, and maybe I was mistaken, but also more hostility? After we spent our mornings writing on the beach with coffee, Mac and I jumped in the ancient, cold water of

Lake Tahoe. We ran to the hot tub, then ran to the showers, and were able to check out on time, adrenaline coursing. We had hours to kill before our midnight flight and so drove to Heavenly, an outdoor shopping area with charming restaurants replete with a gondola ride...*heavenly!* We parked our SUV in the back corner of the underground garage, doing a poor job of it. I checked to make sure the black jeep next to us could get out and saw it had plenty of room.

We shared a strange afternoon, not feeling totally comfortable and suddenly, even urgently, ready to go home to New York. I hadn't found anything to eat at Heavenly, my food anxiety kicking in again. We walked back to the car where I went to the trunk to get my dusty backpack, only to notice on the rearview window someone had spelled O U Y K C U F out of the dust. With our open, tired hearts still racing from the ancient lake, we assumed it was because of the poor parking job, relieved I had seen their expletive before getting in the car, which was how they'd intended it. Mac turned to the passenger side and said, "Oh my god," his voice dropped. I turned the corner to see a swastika on my door, made out of dust.

I found something wet and swiftly wiped it off. We got in and my heart wouldn't slow down; I could see it jumping out of my wrist and chest. I wanted out of this town. I wanted to go home. I was afraid for our safety and our dust-laden car; a once happy give-away of where we had been was now a target.

We stopped at a restaurant before getting on the road back to Reno and I couldn't settle down, wondering who amongst us was a Nazi. Who would make a swastika on our car? I looked at Mac and put my hand on his, noticing the golden, pale complexion. I thought of Eric and Christian, an Asian and Cuban-American couple in love, and how they might feel if they were holding hands here, or if they wouldn't hold hands at all because they didn't have that privilege. If Mac and I, two blue-eyed blondes, could feel our safety threatened just for existing, how would they feel? I thought of Anthony, Instagram Star and out-and-proud Lebanese-Cuban Bear, and Terrell, an African-American hula-hooper: how would either of them feel if a swastika appeared on their car? I had been disparaging the false "equal opportunity" of casting—*sure I present as a straight white woman, but anyone who KNOWS me knows I'm half Iranian, bi-polar, and not straight, so why won't shows like High Maintenance or Orange is the New Black give ME a shot?* I had whined to the car. Some of my friends agreed with me, others offered polite silence. I looked at my sun-kissed "white" skin over Mac's Irish red and was overcome with the realization of our privilege and what it really meant. We could kiss and not be afraid. We could exist here and not be afraid. But I was afraid. Who were they? Who was in the black jeep? Did they really believe in what the swastika represents?

When the Nazis drew their fingers across our passenger door, could they imagine that two days before that I had leaned over that same spot, spreading nuts and berries on desert cooked bread to feed a car of hungry people? Could they imagine *who* sat in those seats and what beautiful conversation and connection had taken place, our love echoing still? Would they ever imagine who we really are?

Valdaniel Martins
lyrics

Exposed

The harder that I ran from you
the more I fell in love with you
and the more I tried to push you away
the more I wished you'd ask me to stay.

And it's so common it doesn't even have a name.
All the consonants and vowels sound the same
and when you try to take a picture from far enough away
all you expose, all you expose is you're afraid.

Coming like a dog back to the door
and the empty dish that fed me once before.
It's empty now with echoes of the things we heard before
we turned our heads to fight this war.

And it's so common it doesn't even have a name.
All the consonants and vowels sound the same
and when you try to keep a picture of everything that has changed
all you expose, all you expose is that I'm afraid
of being loved, I'm afraid of being loved.

I'm afraid of being loved, it's true.
But I hope that, I hope that you can see
I'd like to change that for you.

Dark and Stormy

Trivia

1. The Arabic word *haboob* describes *this* type of intense storm, which can generate speeds up to 62 miles per hour and rise to altitudes of 8,000 feet!

Firsts

2. If you happen to escape the Milky Way and travel for roughly 2.5 million light years, what is the first galaxy you'll hit?

Under the Sea

3. Many creatures that live in the Mariana Trench—the deepest, darkest part of the ocean—rely on *this* chemical reaction in order to see, eat, mate, and communicate.

Literary Villains

4. To avoid plagiarism, the German screenwriter who first brought Bram Stoker's *Dracula* to the cinema had to change the vampire's name. What did he call him instead?

Visual Art

5. Which famous artist said, "I don't do drugs, I am drugs"?

Zachary Parkman
lyrics

Impossible to Hold

You must forgive this hesitation
You're the only soul we've seen in years
And now Sol shines down into our world
Illuminate the darkness, chase away the fears
Breathless anticipation now
Who have we become, have these years below been rewarded by the sky?
So beautiful and so endlessly impossible to...

Hold...onto everything, hold onto the hopes and dreams
When the everyday is so impossible to...
Hold...in your arms again, hold onto you and me
And the possibility

Tell us what of the effort, tell us what of the cause
Are our children still out there fighting?
Do you know my daughter, she's on the southern front
Her silence is so frightening
Have we finally won, have the Terrans turned and fled to the sky?
So wonderful and so endlessly impossible to...

Hold...onto everything, hold onto the hopes and dreams
When the everyday is so impossible to...
Hold...in your arms again, hold onto you and me
And the possibility

This war has taken me, my posterity and left me without
If Sol should refuse to shine, rise into the sky I'll take it as a sign
And, if I lay my body down, down upon the ground let this red
  dust come and bury me
Let it be told let the stories say, here she lays the last casualty of
  a war that never ends

Helen Howard

fiction

novel excerpt from
Aftershock

Prologue

"You think I care what China or Korea have to say? I wasn't elected to bow
to foreigners. I'll go where I please in my own country." Akira Nakagawa,
the sixty-fourth Prime Minister of Japan, smoothed the arms of his black
mourning suit as he added, "The time for apologizing for the Pacific War
is over."

Sitting beside him on the back seat of the Toyota Century sedan,
Kimura, his chief aide, inclined his head respectfully. He handed over a
sheet of paper. "Do you want to take another look at your speech?"

Nakagawa brushed it away. "I know it by heart."

Kimura returned the document to a smooth black folder resting on his
knees. "Their reaction will be immediate."

"And we know exactly what they'll say. That's what I love about the
Chinese, they're so predictable."

They passed the tended hedges and trees lining the wide moat that
circled the stone walls of the Imperial Palace. Along the footpath, people
watched the procession of government cars sweep past. A young girl with
a worldly squint caught Nakagawa's eye, reminding him of his daughter
before she reached the age where her father irritated her.

"The warning makes me nervous," said Kimura.

"It doesn't worry me." Nakagawa glanced out the side window at the
extra security detail trailing the cortege.

Shrewd-looking, with a hawkish nose and swept back hair, Nakagawa
based his election campaign on staking claim to disputed Japanese
territories and tapped into an unexpectedly popular public vein, leading
the party to their strongest election victory in over twenty years. Now he
was paying an official visit to the Yasukuni Shrine, founded in the
nineteenth century to enshrine the spirits of those who fought and died

overseas in wars for Japan, controversially including the spirits of Class-A war criminals from the Second World War. In recent years, Japanese politicians had shied away from visits to the shrine, fearing criticism from South Korea, Taiwan, and—most vocally—China, all of whom took the opportunity to accuse Japan of an arrogant lack of remorse for wartime atrocities.

Nakagawa's much publicized visit was the political equivalent of a raised middle finger across the ocean.

The cortege turned into the shrine. Police motorcycles tore away to block the road and a small army of uniformed men with florescent blinking sticks raced out to wave the Prime Minister's car into the grounds. Reporters, photographers, and a few curious passersby clustered behind waist-high barricades. The Toyota Century stopped at the entrance to the broad, flagged avenue leading to the shrine's main prayer hall.

Nakagawa stepped out and threw a curt wave to the press. They snapped photographs and held aloft recording equipment. But unlike the press of other countries, they did not shout out impertinent questions. The Yasukuni Shrine, however China or Korea viewed it, was a place to respect the dead and not even the most insolent journalist would bring down the tone, not in Japan.

Trailed by Kimura, Nakagawa proceeded up the avenue. He elevated his chin and kept his posture stiff and correct, aware of the cameras following his movements. Click, click, click; photographs that would soon grace the websites of international newspapers and blogging sites, alongside speculative commentary.

They passed under the main gate. Nakagawa saw the elderly Chief Priest, clad in ivory robes, waiting beneath white scalloped curtains imprinted with the Imperial Seal of Japan, hanging dead still in the calm air. A glint of light stabbed his eyes and he squinted, relieved that the press was behind him; a photograph of an uncertain squint could do a great deal to lessen the impact of this visit. Such was politics.

This was his last thought before the shrine shimmered and glazed and he no longer understood whether he was moving forward or backward.

Chapter One

Fingers closed around her neck. Penelope shoved down her chin, rounded her shoulders, and ripped her fingers through his grip, yanked apart his thumbs and rammed down with a rigid fist which landed on his groin with a squishy crunch. One quick elbow to the stomach, then she spun and delivered a hammer-fist strike to his guts.

A sharp grunt puffed from Brian as he staggered back and dropped to the mats on one knee. Behind him, walls lined with black padding delineated the boundaries of this Krav Maga gym, the only one in Tokyo, tucked into a serene pocket of Omotesando. Most men at the gym knew Penelope's delicate features and slender frame belied a strength that could wipe the floor with all of them. Brian had not gotten the memo; he was new to the place, one of a handful of other foreigners.

"You okay?" Penelope asked, berating herself for using too much force. Instinct took over. She shouldn't have let it. An old guilt rippled to the surface. Her breath came in quick gasps.

"You hit me in the nuts," said Brian through gritted teeth.

"I was off-guard," said Penelope, wanting to avoid an argument but not prepared to take the blame for his stupid action. She grabbed a towel, wiped her sweaty face. "That's not on."

Brian pulled himself from the floor. At full height, he had the physique of a rugby player. "You okay?" one of the Japanese men laughingly called over in English.

"Yeah, just got my balls broken by a ballbreaker, that's all." Brian's Scottish brogue was hard for the Japanese to decipher and his comment met with a polite smile of incomprehension.

Penelope's eyes narrowed. Slowly, she said, "Fuck off. Class ended and you jumped me. Now you're crying 'cos you got hit. Grow up."

"I was putting you in a real-life situation, giving you practice."

"What gives you the right to decide I need that?" Her heart rate remained elevated. Penelope bent over, threw her gear into her bag.

Brian tested his groin area with a wince. "I might have to get checked out now."

"Spare me." Penelope threw him a cutting glance over her shoulder.

"Only a bitch goes straight for the soft spots."

Penelope tensed, every atom in her body screaming to kick him in the eye. Instead, she utilized her training in controlling body reactions, telling herself that she could not practice Krav Maga anywhere else in this city, and therefore she had to be cool. She stood, smiled, and said, "Only a limp dick can't take being beat. I hope your soft spots feel better soon though."

Throwing her bag over her shoulder, Penelope turned from Brian's glare and walked away, passing Hiroki, a younger man who made shy conversation with Penelope whenever he could. "You showed him," he said.

"He didn't give me a choice," she replied in fluent Japanese. She spoke the language at home with her mother and as a child had spent summers at her grandparents' house in Osaka. Her Japanese was almost as polished as a native's but she was still considered *gaijin*, an outside person. Many people could tell she was mixed race, but only a few guessed correctly that her sharp cheekbones and well-cut lips hailed from a Japanese mother, her hazel eyes and Roman nose from an all-American father.

"He nearly cried," Hiroki laughed.

They both looked over at Brian, limping to the changing room. "We should not laugh at other people's pain," she said, wagging a finger in Hiroki's face.

"You are right," he replied solemnly.

"But you can at his, just for today." She smiled, patted him on the shoulder and left.

Her motorbike, a red Honda Shadow Spirit, was parked in the tiny lot around the corner. Buying it was an indulgence but when she saw it, Penelope had to get it. Being on a bike equaled freedom; there was no need to interact with anyone, it was faster than a bicycle, and when she was on it was just her and the road; everything else blended into the background. It was like a moving form of meditation.

She gunned the engine and zipped down the long boulevard leading to Shibuya, turning Brian's bitch comment over in her head. Not the best way to start the day. She wasn't in the wrong, but still, Penelope doubted herself. She had ever since that woman's arm broke.

Four years ago, fresh from a year traveling, mired in the boredom of a graduate job at a prestigious accounting firm in New York, Penelope had seen a posting for 'Clandestine Agent' and applied out of curiosity, a character trait her mother often disapprovingly described as 'recklessness' but which Penelope preferred to view as 'risk-taking that most often paid off.' As it did in this case. After several months of hush-hush interviews, Penelope joined a batch of new CIA trainees and commenced her training at the Farm.

At first she was exhilarated. The CIA was not what she'd expected when she asked the universe to deliver her from the boredom of an ordinary office job, but she was happy to take it. Then, one intense night out on exercise in paramilitary training, a disagreement with someone on her team turned into an argument, turned into pushing and in a few confused seconds, led to a broken arm. Penelope cringed every time she thought of that awful crack, always questioned why she had used so much force. She was cleared of intent after a brief disciplinary action but it soured the start of her new career.

Regardless, she stuck it out. Her new life suited her. The work required her to pull people in, then keep them at arm's length, a skill for which she had a natural aptitude. For a year now, she'd been doing that in Tokyo. In contrast to New York's swirling beat of humanity, Tokyo drummed to a different rhythm, with a calmer energy that had deep undercurrents. It intrigued Penelope in a way Washington D.C. never could. In Tokyo, she felt herself settling into a new mode of being: freer, more at ease.

Her apartment was in a sleek new building nestled on a steep hill beside the train tracks. The station was just out of eyeshot but the rumble of train carriages—and announcements from the open-air platform—were a faint but constant aural backdrop. Penelope loved the wide balcony from which she could peer at life in the surrounding eclectic mix of buildings: tiny restaurants teetering above hair salons, washing hung on many balconies, smokers appearing on outside stairwells.

She threw her gear in the washing machine and jumped in the shower. She had to hurry, she was due to meet Ryo Kanda for coffee in just over an hour. They had met three nights ago in the Milky Way, one of many tiny 'snack bars' that pollinated the areas around train stations, providing fertile hunting ground for her recruitment efforts. Small and basic inside, they offered a limited alcohol selection and a karaoke system for lonely souls, misfits, and salarymen who'd missed the last train to sing the early morning hours away. It was easier to poke through the veil of Japanese opaqueness after a shared drunken rendition of "Twist and Shout." By the end of the night she knew all about Kanda's job in the Ministry of Foreign Affairs, his two children and hostile ex-wife, and decided to try adding him to her stable of agents.

Penelope applied makeup and stepped into a cream pencil dress, figure-hugging with long sleeves. She scooped her hair into a loose ponytail and examined her reflection. Demure and appealing, a good daytime look to tempt a middle-aged bureaucrat. She'd invited Kanda to coffee using the details on the business card he had handed her at the Milky Way. He responded, accepted. In her experience, men were easily swayed into doing something they shouldn't by a pretty face. There was often a midlife crisis waiting to be ignited, an aching hole to be tapped into, a powerful and destructive urge to be picked out and made special. And nothing made men feel more special than attention from an attractive woman.

Penelope hadn't always been attractive. She'd avoided the pitfalls of being pretty too early. By the time she'd grown into her face and her skinniness became a slender frame with well-formed breasts, she knew her own mind. She allowed only one man into her life for five years, until she had to make a choice, and she chose to go ahead alone. Just like her father all those years ago. She never consciously intended to emulate him, but walking away was easier than being left behind. Perhaps some things were just in the blood.

At Shibuya, Penelope boarded the JR train heading north on the loop line. Kanda had chosen the location: a large branch of Doutor, a coffee-shop franchise serving bitter lattes and finger style cheesecakes, near Shinjuku station, three stops away. Penelope sat at a table on the narrow strip of terrace outside. Rainy season was approaching, but the sky was a hard blue dome and humidity was low; this would be one of the last true spring days, warm and friendly.

She saw Kanda approach, a generic businessman emerging from a crowd of other black-suited, black-haired men and women. He gave her a wave before going into the coffee shop, emerging a minute later with a small cup. Penelope stood to greet him, smiling widely. "Nice to see you again," she said in Japanese, bowing slightly.

"Nice to see you too." In the light of day Kanda looked less buoyant than he did bellowing, "I can't get no satisfaction" into the microphone at the Milky Way. Penelope guessed him to be in his late forties by the pinched skin around his eyes. "I didn't expect to hear from you."

"Oh, really? Well, I just thought it would be good to make another professional connection."

"That is very kind."

"I appreciate you coming. It can be hard to make friends in Tokyo." Penelope could sometimes pass as full Japanese, especially in a dark bar when someone was not paying much attention, but she told him she was American when he asked where she came from. Best not to start out lying too much with a person you intended to build some kind of professional relationship with. She didn't tell him her real name though. She never told them her real name.

Waylen Roche
lyrics

Soul of a Rider

She told me "don't be so passive aggressive about it,
I come from a family that lacks communication."
I'm sorry you're hurting, I'm worried the story
Shouldn't be without a taste of anticipation.

I want to bring life into the world with you, but I'm so scared of
   the insanity that marks our situation.
You gotta choose the kind of shoes you're wearing when you're
   running through, this tangle of calamity and negative
   vibrations.

But I say...

Alright, drive through the night, make every night, soul of a rider.
Hypnotized, ghosts in our eyes are changing our minds, souls and
   horizons.

I wish I could say I've figured out the world today,
Why so little love? Why so much hate and separation?
It's all I can do just to keep moving to
the rhythm of the city streets, the dreams that I am chasing.

But I say...

Alright, drive through the night, make every night, soul of a rider.
Hypnotized, ghosts in our eyes are changing our minds, souls and
   horizons.

Amy Dupcak

fiction

Siren Song

I see her running—a whirlwind of a girl. She blows like ash across the avenue, six lanes wide. The cars will stop for her I'm sure.

Her hair's overgrown. A homemade necklace of ribbons, stones, and bones bounces off her chest. She wears red vintage boots with half-sewn soles and half-tied laces, a lacy black slip, and a man's blazer with professorial elbow pads. I only met Gemma three days ago, but it feels like I've known her for years. When she reaches me, we hug and kiss and step into the club's black velvet curtain.

Beneath disco-ball stars, we dance like no one's watching even though they are. New York wouldn't care, but Los Angeles *stares*. Still, we go at it, the only girls who dare. Politely, we make requests: "Iggy Pop, Depeche Mode, Siouxsie Sioux, please?" Birds of a feather, the same songs etch our wings. But this smirking DJ doesn't abide, simply shrugs his shoulders and swats us like flies. The melodies forsake us.

Our trio of boys make jokes, slug drinks, and urge us to stir the embers of their egos. Gemma knows them from LA; I know them from New York. They were different people there: looser with language yet tenser in the jaw. Here, they fake-cry on film and recite monologues on floodlit stages. They pose for my camera wearing ironic hats and the booze-stained suits they slept in. Earlier, I sat alone on their patchwork lawn as the January sun played catch with the moon across a hot pink sky. I wore Asher's hoodie with the broken zipper and found three cigarettes in the depths of a pocket. I placed them, one after the next, between the ridges of my teeth, inhaling glass, smoke, ghosts.

Now Asher and the boys pull cigarettes from behind their ears like birthday-party magicians. They say, "Let's move on," so we follow-the-leader in a winding conga line. Basking under unseen stars, Gemma glows in the dark. Does anyone else see?

We find ourselves in another club on the notorious strip. Another dance floor without dancers. Another haze of hairspray and aftershave. Another DJ blasting ambivalence. Boys try to butter us up, buy us new drinks, gaze into our glassy eyes. Somewhere between leather jackets, whorls of heat, and waves of sound, I lose Gemma. But then her silky hand finds mine, fingers entwined as we dash outside.

"Can we bum a smoke?" she asks some man in a fedora—a hat with no sense of irony.

"Are you sisters?"

We laugh. "Yeah, we're twins!"

He nods and cocks his head. "Can you read each other's minds? Think of a number. A color."

We laugh again and skip to the corner. She sucks the borrowed cigarette to the bone, then passes it to me; I send my smoke rings up to the waxy moon. Everything in this city's wrapped in cellophane, a lacquered sheen. I almost love it.

At the club's entrance, Gemma pauses, lips curled tight. "Let's just leave."

"And go where?" I ask.

"Anywhere!"

"What about the boys?" I've been crashing at their place for days, sleeping on a mattress pumped with stale air.

"Who cares," Gemma declares. And that decides it.

We race each other across the avenue, all six lanes wide, to find her parked car. It's small and silver, banged-up and bruised. A wounded thing, but well-loved. Duct-tape decorates the dashboard and a saint medallion dangles from the rearview mirror: Saint Jude, Patron Saint of Lost Causes. I should have known.

She checks both ways, pulls out, and off we go at top speed. Her grin glows golden; you can't fake this kind of manic glee. A cassette tape purrs and a familiar voice sings, *I am the passenger, and I ride and I ride.*

Sometimes, patterns are too perfect to chalk up to coincidence. Sometimes, you're no longer a "you" but an ephemeral "we," more than the sum of your parts. Sometimes, a girl named Gemma Lowe cranks the volume on a song you both need. Four centuries ago, Puritan men would have burned her alive.

"Where to?" she shouts over Iggy's callused voice.

"Anywhere!" comes my belated echo.

Pumped with adrenaline and estrogen, our destination's irrelevant. Fluorescent lights blur like moons in my eyes as we trace this city's neon spine.

All of it was made for you and me, 'cause it belongs to you and me, so let's take a ride and see what's mine.

What's *ours*, I want to say. Let's take this night and stretch it long, like one unending dream. Let's read tarot at Cielo, stamp our names into Hollywood cement, and dance like banshees at the Roosevelt, where Marilyn blew her final kiss. *La la la.*

"Siouxsie sings it better," Gemma proclaims, rummaging through the console to choose a different cassette. She throws Iggy to the backseat and I know I'm in for a treat.

We accelerate again, her half-sewn sole to the pedal as synths rise like steam and a woman's voice sings liquid silver. It's not the cover song, no, *but ohh, oh your city lies in dust.* Yes, we are leaving them in the dust, all the boys who poke and smirk and lap us up. The past is good as dead to us.

Am I in love with Gemma Lowe? Or is this deeper than love, deeper than flashing lights and teenage dreams and terrazzo stars of fame? She takes my hand, her palm-lines a spiderweb pulling me close. Her eyes find mine and cast a spell, a moment inside a moment inside ourselves. The stars have aligned for our star-crossed fate, a swirling escape. *But oh...*

This silver voice belongs to us: our poem, our prayer, our chance to shine. These night-slick streets might diverge at any time. I look at the cars we pass and imagine another pair of us—two girls in motion, two stars in the making, too young to know better and too old to care—racing another pair in another car on a parallel street in a parallel city, our shadows dancing in an endless parade as time splits its seams.

So what if I never go back to my city? What if this ride never ends? We may be lost causes, but our souls sing a siren song. We can press rewind and leave everything behind.

Italicized lyrics by Iggy Pop and Siouxsie Sioux

Contributors

Sheila-Joon Azim (aka Joon) is a New York based actor who loves words and occasionally sings at parties. She has appeared at Primary Stages, The Cherry Lane, The Duke Theatre, George St. Playhouse and The McCarter Theatre, etc. Favorite roles include Belle in *Onaje* (Fringe '18), Violante in *Double Falsehood* (Judith Shakespeare), and Claire/Valerie in *Carefully Taught* (APAC). With a passion for mental health and wellness in the arts, Joon recently became a certified yoga teacher and is currently working on her book, *Leave Your Objects at the Door*, a personal exploration in re-narration.

Mac Barrett, many years ago, published a few stories, poems, essays, and reviews here and there, in places like *The Brooklyn Rail, Anderbo, The Rumpus, 32 Poems,* and *Salon.* He is the Curator of Public Programming at Roosevelt House Public Policy Institute of Hunter College.

Brian Birnbaum graduated from Sarah Lawrence College with an MFA in Fiction. His first novel, *Emerald City,* came out with Dead Rabbits in September 2019. Brian is a child of Deaf adults (CODA) and works in development for the family sign language interpreting business. He lives in Harlem with the writer M.K. Rainey and their dog. www.briansbirnbaum.com

Adam Blotner Is a writer/performer and creator of Pop Filter, a musical comedy act that satirizes pop music with original songs and characters. Pop Filter has appeared in the Edinburgh Festival Fringe, NY International Fringe Festival, Feinstein's/54 Below, LA Comedy Festival, NYC Comedy Week, NY Funny Songs Festival, and rocked the STAPLES Center at an LA Kings Game. His viral videos have appeared in the *Huffington Post, Funny or Die, CAFE, Medium,* and *Broadway World,* with over 14 million views. In 2018 he released the album *Step to the Left: Country for Liberals.* www.adamblotner.com

Emily Brout lives and works in New York and has written many short stories, one of which was recommended by Etgar Keret, translated into Hebrew and published in *Maaboret*. She thinks this is pretty damn cool and may act as a psychic atonement for never having been Bat Mitzvahed. She has also written for *Electric Literature, Tom Tom Magazine, Feminine Collective, Flock, Pigeon Pages,* and the *New York Observer.*

Britt Canty received her MFA in Creative Writing from The New School. Her work has appeared in *The Rumpus, Vol. 1 Brooklyn, Heavy Feather Review,* and other places. Britt is a curator for HIP Lit and a member of the Board of Directors for *Epiphany Magazine*. She lives in Brooklyn.

Jessica Delfino is a comedian, writer, musician and mom who lives in NYC. Her comedy has been featured in the *New York Times, Glamour, Mashable,* ABC's *Good Morning America* and more. Her writing has been in *The Atlantic, McSweeney's, The Week, High Times, SELF Magazine* and on her top parenting blog, Medium.com/@OneAndDoneMom. Her dulcet tones have been heard on Dr. Demento, Howard Stern with Little Mikey, The Red Peters Show, and SiriusXM. In her spare time, she loves to dig crystals, ride her bicycle and hang out with her husband, son and cat. Find her on Instagram or Twitter: @JessicaDelfino.

Sean Dunne: "I grew up drinking Forties and smoking bud with my friends. These things hurt us. They cheapened our punk rock ideals and rendered generic the dreams which otherwise might have been quite profound. I've never been able to get over that. So I guess with my writing, I'm just trying to make good on the things we said we were going to do."

Amy Dupcak is the author of *Dust, Short Stories* (2016). Her fiction and creative nonfiction were published in *Sonora Review, Phoebe, Hypertext, Fringe, Litro, Bookanista,* and other journals, and her poems have appeared in *District Lit, Pangyrus, The Night Heron Barks,* and *Alternative Field & Avenue 50 Studio's* "Poetry in Isolation" chapbook. She earned her MFA in Fiction from The New School and has been a creative and essay writing instructor at Writopia Lab since 2012, primarily working with teens. Currently, she also freelance edits and tutors, teaches fiction for adults at The Writer's Rock, acts as an assistant editor of *Cagibi*, and crafts original themed trivia for every Lyrics, Lit & Liquor event.

Rachel Evans is a writer, actress, and high school drama teacher. For two years she was the monthly dating columnist for *NY Blueprint*. Her one-woman show, *Jew Wish*, premiered in the NY Fringe Festival and was subsequently performed at The Eldridge Street Synagogue and Planet Connections. Her short plays and monologues have had readings or performances at various theaters in NYC. She's had a personal essay appear on *Kveller*, and has another forthcoming in the book *Sex With Everybody* from Little Brown & Co. She thinks Lyrics, Lit & Liquor is a super great event, and she's a big fan of Amanda Miller and Amy Dupcak.

Juliet Fletcher's nonfiction essays, reporting and news analysis have appeared in *Philadelphia City Paper, The Herald* (Glasgow, Scotland), *The Brian Lehrer Show, The Record* (N.J.) and elsewhere. As a fiction writer, she sits on the board of the Mystery Writers of America (New York chapter) where she organizes events for emerging writers, and is working on her first novel of political suspense.

Jordana Frankel is a creative writing instructor at Writopia Lab and the author of two young adult novels (*The Ward*, 2013 & *The Isle*, 2016). She received her BA from Goucher College and an MFA in Creative Writing from Hollins University. She's currently writing a TV pilot.

Christie Grotheim's personal essays and creative nonfiction have been featured in *Salon, The New York Observer, Mr. Beller's Neighborhood, Ducts, Smithmag,* and *The Reset*. After taking creative writing courses at The New School's Eugene Lang College of Liberal Arts, she took classes at the 92Y, first dabbling in poetry and then venturing into fiction, which grabbed hold of her and didn't let go until she'd completed a novel. The character Marjorie Moore was conceived there in the Advanced Fiction workshop—where the story was voted best in the class—and now, a few years later, Christie has birthed her debut novel: *The Year Marjorie Moore Learned to Live*, published by Heliotrope. www.christiegrotheim.com

Jared Harél is the author of *Go Because I Love You* (Diode Editions, 2018) and *The Body Double* (Brooklyn Arts Press, 2012). He's been awarded the Stanley Kunitz Memorial Prize from *American Poetry Review*, the William Matthews Poetry Prize from *Asheville Poetry Review,* and two Individual Artist Grants from Queens Council on the Arts. His poems have appeared in such journals as *32 Poems, Massachusetts Review, The Southern Review, Tin House* and *Threepenny Review*. Harél plays drums, teaches writing at Nassau Community College, and lives in Queens, NY with his wife and two kids. Stop by: www.jaredharel.com

Scott Alexander Hess is the author of five novels, including *Skyscraper*, a Lambda Literary Award Finalist, and *The Butcher's Sons*, which was named a Kirkus Reviews Best Book of 2015. His writing has appeared in *HuffPost, Genre Magazine, The Fix, Thema Literary Review,* and elsewhere. Hess co-wrote "Tom in America," an award-winning short film, starring Sally Kirkland and Burt Young. He teaches fiction writing at Gotham Writers Workshop and curates *Hot Lit*, an LGBTQ+ themed monthly newsletter. Originally from St. Louis, Missouri, Hess lives in New York City with his husband. www.scottalexanderhess.com

Helen Howard was born in England but left as soon as she could and never stopped going. After living in Japan for five years and Singapore for another five, she moved to New York to see what all the fuss was about. She has called the Big Apple home for the past three years and is surprised to have finally found a home. She is working on her second novel, a political thriller set in Japan.

Nancy Hightower has written essays on spirituality and politics, mental health, as well as the #MeToo movement. Her essays, fiction, and poetry have appeared in journals such as *Joyland, Entropy, Vol. 1 Brooklyn*

storySouth, Sundog Lit, and *Sojourners,* among others. Her debut novel, *Elementarí Rising* (2013), received a starred review in *Library Journal* and was chosen as Debut of the Month. Her poetry collection, *The Acolyte* (Port Yonder Press, 2015), offers a feminist interpretation of biblical narratives, and she is currently working on a memoir about growing up in the evangelical South. She is on the board of directors for *Epiphany Magazine.* www.nancyhightower.com

Matt Litwack (drinks illustrator) is a commercial mural artist born and raised in NYC. He has run his company Intelligentgraffiti.com for eleven years and has painted murals around the world.

Meher Manda is a poet, short story writer, culture critic, and educator from Mumbai, India, currently based in New York City. She earned her MFA in Creative Writing from the College of New Rochelle where she founded the literary journal *The Canopy Review.* Her debut chapbook of poetry, *Busted Models,* was published by No, Dear Magazine in Fall 2019. Her fiction and poetry have appeared in *Epiphany, Los Angeles Review, Glass Poetry, Lumina, Newtown Literary,* and is forthcoming in *Hobart, Pulp,* and *They Rise Like A Wave: An Anthology of Asian American Poetry.* She is currently at work on her debut poetry manuscript and a short story collection, both centered around Indian women.

Valdaniel Martins is a singer/songwriter, subway performer and writer. Citing influences from Irish folk to soul to Latin and African rhythms, Valdaniel loops songs, spoken-word and multiple instruments together to weave a rich cord both tethered in and embellishing the folk songwriter tradition. https://valdaniel.com

Amanda Miller is a writer and actor who published her memoir, *One Breath, Then Another* on Lucid River Press (2013) and whose writing has appeared in *The Rumpus, Freerange Nonfiction, Cratelit, So Long: Short Memoirs of Loss and Remembrance, Underwired Magazine* and more. She recently served on the Nonfiction committee for PEN America's Prison

Writing Contest. Amanda has performed her solo plays *The Jew in the Ashram* and *How To Suffer Better* nationally and internationally at a variety of theater festivals and venues including the Edinburgh Fringe, Edmonton Fringe, Whitefire Theatre's Solofest and The People's Improv Theater's Solocom. She earned an MFA in Creative Writing from The New School and a BFA in Acting from NYU and has produced, curated, and hosted Lyrics, Lit & Liquor since 2012. www.thejewintheashram.com, www.howtosufferbetter.com

Noam Osband is a media producer and anthropologist. He writes funny songs dealing with real life stories. Visit him: http://www.noamosband.com

Zachary Parkman is a Brooklyn based singer songwriter who blends traditional folk with indie prog-rock themes about love, existential dread, and the colonization of Mars. When not performing in the pop-up a cappella group, The Bear & The Bee, with his one-and-a-half-year-old daughter (on Brooklyn street corners, bodegas, and Subway stations) he can be found performing with the brooding Americana duo The Darkest Timeline, the Washington, DC based indie prog band Bad Robot Jones, and the space opera sci-fi folk group Here Lies The Human Race.

Kyle Pritz used the G.I. Bill, after leaving the U.S. Marines in 2012 as a conscientious objector, to earn a B.S. in Psychology and a B.A. in Philosophy at Fordham University, where he learned nothing except that his true love was poetry, its craft and its question (what is poetry?). He's a grassroots community organizer of progressive military veterans. He was a runner up for the #DignityNotDetention Outside Poetry Prize 2019 and the 2019 Julia Darling Memorial Poetry Prize by Kallisto Gaia Press. He has been published in *Chronogram* and other spaces. He actively participates in a number of poetry communities around New York state, including Supa Dupa Fresh.

Joel Remland isn't a writer, but he's had some memorable experiences that make for good stories, which his partner Amy encouraged him to develop into brief memoir pieces. On a younger set of legs, he toured the US and Canada extensively, playing guitar, bass, and singing in DIY indie/punk bands, and can still play almost any rock song after hearing it once. He's a consummate traveler, having visited 35+ countries and taught English in Bangkok for a stint. He has also attended Burning Man eleven times, establishing his group as a recognized theme camp at the annual festival. Joel earned his Master's in International Education and currently manages operations for the education department at City Parks Foundation.

Waylen Roche is a multi-instrumentalist singer-songwriter, producer and performance curator sharing his time between Brooklyn and Newburgh, NY. Roche weaves together inflections of contemporary classical, alt R&B and jazz in his compositions, which he has performed across NYC in various groups such as Noise Downstairs and the Paper Souls. Roche is currently producing music for a progressive political podcast called The SGNL, and when not making music enjoys improv comedy, motorcycle riding, hiking, and walking his cats on leashes around his farm upstate.

Megan Sass is a writer, comedian, and actor. She has contributed sketches and satirical articles to The NBC Diversity Showcase, *Reductress*, Spoiled Media, and *Heeb Magazine.* Her video sketches have been featured on *CollegeHumor, Gothamist, HuffPo UK, Laughing Squid, Funny or Die, Elite Daily, WhoHaha,* and more. She is the co-creator/playwright of the *Time Out NY Critic's Pick* musical *The Mad Scientist's Guide To Romance, Robots, and Soul-Crushing Loneliness.* She has been a regular performer with sketch teams Victory Cereal and Terrorbird, as Sarah Huckabee Sanders/Angela Merkel on Adam Hamway's *Jimmy Fallon's The Tonight Show,* and with her own show, *The Outer Zone* at The People's Improv Theatre. She is currently a series writer for the webseries *Redheads Anonymous.* @Megan_Sass

Christopher X. Shade is author of the novel *The Good Mother of Marseille* (2019) and the book of poems *Shield the Joyous* (2020). He is co-founder and co-editor of *Cagibi*, at cagibilit.com, a journal of poetry and prose. His stories and book reviews have appeared widely, and he has won story awards including the 2016 Writers at Work fellowship competition. He teaches fiction and poetry writing at The Writers Studio. Raised in the South, he now lives with his wife in New York City. His debut book of poems *Shield the Joyous*, forthcoming April 2020, is about the loss of loved ones to the disease of addiction. https://christopherxshade.com

Shawn Shafner is a Brooklyn-based artist, educator and activist. He founded The People's Own Organic Power (POOP) Project in 2010 and has since created numerous theatrical works, educational programs, online videos, installations and community-based projects, podcast episodes, and more. For his work, Shawn has been featured as a Waste Warrior on CBC Radio One, interviewed for articles in the *New York Post* and *DNA Info*, and The POOP Project has been profiled in *The Huffington Post*, *Buzzfeed*, *American Hipster*, Good.com, *TreeHugger*, and *Broadway World*. https://thepoopproject.org

Melissa Shaw is a writer, theater artist, and humorist from Brooklyn, New York. Her work has appeared in *Alma* and *Medium*, and she is a member of Moxie Sketch Lab at the Magnet Theater. Melissa is an associate artist with Falconworks Artist Group. She holds an MFA from Sarah Lawrence College.

Simi Toledano is a first-generation American actress, director, solo performer, writer, teaching artist, and ritual leader. She has written and performed her personal stories of healing and transformation as a solo performer at NYC venues such as BRIC, The Triad, Dixon Place, and Big Irv's. Most recently, she served as creator/performer in the devised play *This is How Girls Die* with the Paperdoll Ensemble in Philadelphia. She is the writer, director and co-producer of her first short film *Moondance*, which is currently in post-production and set to be released by the end of 2019. Simi serves as a new moon ceremony facilitator and is currently training at the Kohenet Hebrew Priestess Institute.

Jenny Williamson is a poet and fiction writer living in Brooklyn. Her work is published in journals including *East Coast Literary Review, Diode, Arsenic Lobster, Vox Poetica,* and elsewhere. Her poetry chapbook, *Collection of Flaws in a Black Dress,* was published by Finishing Line Press in 2016, and she is the co-host of the *Ancient History Fangirl* podcast. More of her work can be found here: www.jennywilliamson.com

Trivia Answers

Pale Ale
1. Drunk
2. "Tubthumping" by Chumbawamba
   (it's not called "I Get Knocked Down")
3. The Situationists
4. *Do the Right Thing*
5. Mercury

Cabernet
1. Milk
2. Juliet was an angel and Romeo was a knight
3. Harpy
4. Frida Kahlo
5. A lock of pubic hair

Dirty Martini
1. Lipstick
2. Succubus
3. "Justify my Love" performed by Madonna
4. Phallic stage
5. Condom

Bloody Mary
1. Shere Khan from *The Jungle Book*
2. *The Giver*
3. *Yesterday and Today*
4. "Little Red Riding Hood"
5. Pig's blood

Tequila Shot
1. Lexington
2. Sid and Nancy
3. Tardigrades (also called water bears)
4. North Korea
5. Caligula

Shirley Temple
1. A virgin
2. Hopscotch
3. Judy Blume
4. *Beauty and the Beast*
5. Happy Meals

Whiskey Neat
1. Abracadabra
2. Mescaline
3. A feather
4. Abraham Lincoln
5. Go

Dark and Stormy
1. Dust storm, or wall of dust
2. Andromeda
3. Bioluminescence
4. Count Orlok
   (Nosferatu is not the vampire's name)
5. Salvador Dali

Made in the USA
Middletown, DE
11 September 2020